THE
FUTILE LIFE
OF PITO PEREZ

JOSÉ RUBÉN ROMERO

THE FUTILE LIFE OF PITO PEREZ

TRANSLATED FROM THE ORIGINAL SPANISH (LA VIDA INÚTIL DE PITO PÉREZ)

BY

WILLIAM O. CORD

DRAWINGS BY PEDRO A. NOA

PRENTICE-HALL, INC.,
ENGLEWOOD CLIFFS, NEW JERSEY

Second printing.......March, 1967

Preface

To speak adequately of an author is a difficult task, and doubly so when—as in this case—the author happens to be one's own father.

Any praise I might give of my father's work, already so well-known throughout all the Spanish-American countries, would be like trying to make nature's sun even brighter with our own feeble light. Suffice it to say that with this first complete and unabridged version in English of *La vida inútil de Pito Pérez*, a wholly and thoroughly Mexican personage is introduced to a new world. He is a character beloved and intimately understood by Mexicans and other Latin Americans alike because we have found self-identification in much of his belief and thought. And, because time and man have proved that Pito

Pérez is indeed a character of universal qualities, in reality he crosses all language barriers and belongs to all cultures of our epoch.

Recording Pito's story in words, my father wandered with him, arm in arm, along the paths of life as he conversed, philosophized, reflected on matters of human concern, and proudly spoke his piece. But, my father also gave us Pito in his moments of loneliness and he showed us Pito's profound capacity for love of all mankind. And these finer characteristics of Pito Pérez are really a mirror which reflects the soul and spirit of José Rubén Romero, the gentleman, the diplomat, the humorist—one who recognized in his protagonist a greatness of man and hence gave him literary birth.

I wish to express my sincere appreciation to Dr. William O. Cord for his very magnificent translation of this work. I would hope that his work reaches the hearts and minds of those of his world as has the original within its own culture. I would also hope that the book's profoundly human message reaches the English-reading public with the same passionate urgency with which it captivated those of my father's culture who have read and re-read so many times his words and his story of Pito Pérez.

Mexico, D. F.   *Carlos Romero*
Republic of Mexico
June 30, 1966

I have no determined spot
In which to die, and to be born,
And I wander always, forlorn,
Never knowing where I am to rest.

Calderón de la Barca

Part One

"Oh, the poor Devil.
What pity I feel for him."
Pito Perez

The dark silhouette of a man was plainly outlined in the luminous arch of the bell tower. It was Pito Perez, intently absorbed in his contemplation of the surrounding countryside.

His bulky, ill-fitting shoes had come apart and they seemed to grimace as if in pain. His pants appeared to have been made of cobwebs and his jacket, fastened in front with a safety pin, cried out for help through all its open seams. But its pleas did not stir the pity of the people. An old, broad-rimmed straw hat formed a golden halo around his head.

Beneath these miserable rags was seen an even more wretched body with its rough, colorless skin.

The face, pale and lean, seemed to be that of an ascetic wasted away by fasting and religious vigils.

"What are you doing here in the tower, Pito Perez?"

"I came to fish for memories, with the view as my bait."

"Well, I came to hammer out poetic imagery in the forge of twilight."

"Am I bothering you?"

"Good Heavens no, man. Am I in your way?"

"Not in the least. We came up into this tower with different goals in mind and each of us, in his own way, will achieve his end: you, the poet withdrawing from the world long enough to search for rhymes for your sonnets, those fourteen trembling, little birds; I drawing close to my village, to see it, to feel it once again before leaving, perhaps for good; to take with me the memory of all its little nooks and corners, its streets and roads and byways, its gardens, its hills. Perhaps, perhaps never again will I see them!"

"Once again the wanderlust, Pito Perez?"

"What else? I am a restless Pito, a restless dingus who will never strike it rich. Believe me, I don't want to go. I swear it. I'm trying not to leave this land which after all is very much mine, very much a part of me. Ah! Canuto's tasty tidbits! And Aunt Susa's stew! And the coconut tortes that Lino, the baker makes! But, I have just come off a long and fateful

4

drunken binge and my relatives want to get rid of me, as does everyone else. Everything around me proves it to me: the stores won't give me credit any more; my friends don't invite me to their get-togethers; and the Mayor treats me as if I were the world's worst criminal. Why do you think he doubled this last jail term I just finished serving? Well, only because I made an innocent comment at the moment I was being sentenced to the tank. He gave out with his solemn sentence: 'Pito Perez, for being drunk and outraging the public decency, ten dollars fine, or thirty days.' To which I answered with all due civility: 'But, sir, what are you going to do with your dingus holed up so long?' The Mayor blasted me with all the artillery of his authority, sentencing me to clean the prisoners' latrines for three nights in a row. Haven't you ever noticed that the profession of being a tyrant is much easier than being a physician or a lawyer? First year: an endless cycle of promises, smiles, and courteous words to those who elected him; second year: ending old friendships or paying off old friends to avoid being reminded of the past by their presence creating a Supreme Council of Brown Nosers; third year: complete courses in self-worship and delusions of grandeur; fourth and final year: complete predominance of personal opinions and abuses of all kinds. After four years the Degree of Tyrant begins to become quite repulsive to everyone and no university would dare revalidate it."

5

"You are quite intelligent, Pito Perez. One can scarcely find reasons as to why you waste your life away drinking, carousing, and censuring others."

"I'm a friend of Truth. And, if I get loaded, it is for no other reason than to bolster my courage to speak it out. But as you know, from the mouths of babes and drunks. . . . Add to all this the fact that I really do hate and despise the privileged classes."

"Come on over. Sit down. Let's talk as if we were old friends."

"Suits me. Our conversation could be titled: *Dialogue between a Poet and a Madman*."

We sat down on the outside edge of the tower with our legs dangling down. My new shoes, next to Pito's, were well polished and they shone with that foolish pride of the rich. In fact, they had such a shine that Pito looked at them very scornfully and I felt the full impact of his stare. Our feet epitomized our entire social world filled with its injustices and inequalities.

"Why did you say that our conversation would be a dialogue between a poet and a madman?"

"Because you boast of being a poet and everybody here in town thinks of me as a plain old incurable idiot. They swear that there's a screw loose in my whole family. That's a good one! They are sure that my sisters, Herlinda and Maria, suffer from some religious disease and because of it they never leave the church. The people swear that Concha is off her rocker because she spends all her time teaching street dogs to sit on their hind paws, and her brown and white cat to eat at the table with all the grace of a real gentleman. They say that Josefa threw herself down a well, head first, because she was crazy. And Dolores fell in love with a circus performer for the same reason, according to the infallible conclusions of those Holy Fathers who run loose around here. My brother, Joaquin, the priest, won't hear confessions from the zealous females because he's wacky, and I get crocked and I sing and I cry and I walk through the streets with my clothes torn to shreds because I'm nuts! What idiotic logic! Those who live without the will to live, those who live only because they are afraid to die, they are the crazy ones! Those who try to hide their true feelings, they are the crazy ones! And those who would like to run off with a circus performer but don't dare because of what others might say, they are the crazy ones! And those who torture harmless animals instead of teaching them to love man, they are the crazy ones! Isn't that so, Brother Francis Assisi? Those who kneel before some joker who is really their equal, some wiseacre who mumbles Latin and wears a cassock, just to tell him obscenities—like those washerwomen who go down to the creek every Saturday to wash their blouses, knowing full well that next week they will be back to do the same thing because they have only one blouse—they are the crazy ones! And even crazier

7

than I are those people who do not laugh, or cry, or drink, because they are slaves to useless social customs! I prefer my mixed-up family and not that flock of hypocrites who see me as a black sheep simply because I don't sleep on their dunghill or bah in unison with all the others."

"But, it is one thing for some to think you mad and quite another for you to live so oddly—and please excuse me for speaking to you so frankly—without your honorable family reputation meaning anything to you. For what end does your intelligence serve you?"

"Intelligence! The hell you say! The only thing that is certain, and you won't believe this, is that I am a real wretch. My bad luck has followed me since the day I was born and everything I try comes out just the reverse from what I wanted. But, don't think that I drink because of that! I get drunk because I like to—and for no other reason. If I have any talents, I use them to find a means to get my drinks free. That way, I get double pleasure. Oh, how I enjoyed that time when I drank a whole barrel of grain alcohol in Flores' tavern. And without anyone realizing how crafty I really was! I'll tell you how I did it just in case some day you want to make use of my trick.

"In Flores' tavern, the barrels of wine serve as backs for the customers' chairs. Knowing this, I used to go there every night and, completely sober, I would sit down near one of the barrels. After some time of idle chitchat, I would get to my feet, always with some difficulty and always talking with a thick tongue. And, night after night, the owners would say: 'That Pito Perez! He really gets soused! He comes in stone sober and crawls out on all fours!' And it was true. I had to go down the street on all fours so I wouldn't lose my way home, sometimes meowing like a cat and other times barking like a dog—and so lifelike, that the real animals followed me and tried to fool around with me. The real secret of my binges was this: With a corkscrew I was able to make a hole in the cork of the barrel and in it I put a piece of thin tubing which, hidden beneath my coat, brought to my mouth the comfort of that tasty liquid which, from so much drinking, was quickly liquidated forever. With a blob of sap from a log-wood tree, I disguised the hole. (It's a pity that others can't plug up their own holes the same way.) The vice of wine is terrible, my friend, for as a starting point, a sot must lose all sense of decency. It takes a lot to lose it, but when one is freed of it how relaxed, how unworried he is. As they say, one of the best known shameless bastards of Mexico has preached."

"Tell me something about your life, Pito Perez."

"I can't now because I have to keep a date with a friend who has offered to buy me a few drinks. It would be sacrilegious not to take advantage of such a great opportunity."

9

"Then, let's make a deal: Come here every afternoon and then, when we climb back down the tower, I'll pay for your conversation with a bottle."

"Anything I want? Cognac? Champagne? But, don't get frightened. Those drinks are for the wealthy immigrants who really don't love our country. I imagine that those who drink these things are like those Mexicans who went to Europe to bring back an emperor as fair as champagne.

"It is necessary to make use of what a country produces: To govern us: a dark-skinned man, like Juarez; to drink: from Puruaran, tequila or charanda or aguardiente, the offspring of the sugar cane, which indeed is as noble as the grape. I assure you that if Mass were consecrated with aguardiente, the priests would be more humble and more kindly with their flocks."

"OK. Since you are such a unique character, I will pay you, for each hour of conversation, with a bottle of that Puruaran aguardiente which you praise so highly. We human beings are cruel in this respect: we offer a drink to a hungry man, but never a piece of bread."

"And do you think you're going to have a good time listening to me, and that my life is a mosaic of witty remarks? Or a little music box that plays only happy tunes? My life is a sad one, like that of all cheats. But, I have seen people laugh so often at my sorrow that I have ended up laughing at it myself,

10

thinking that my pain will not be so bitter since it affords some pleasure to others. I'm on my way now to find my benefactor because I never renege on a deal to drink at someone else's expense. Tomorrow it's your turn, as we have agreed."

And Pito Perez disappeared down the spiral stairway of the tower, like a dirty penny disappears into the slot of the collection box.

Pito Perez kept his appointment on the dot. He was dressed as on the day before, but in addition he wore a detachable, celluloid collar, a wide, stiff tie, which, if it looked like some kind of breast protector, was really more like a smashed bird's nest, and a red carnation in his lapel—red, like a bloodstain on his dirty coat.

The sun also resembled a carnation, one about to burst, one which clung to the lacelike veil of the heavens.

"You look quite elegant, Pito Perez."

"You bet your boots I do! Not even my mother would recognize me. The bad part is that my suit doesn't match my shoes and my hat is a little small for me because the dead man from whom I took it was less of a bighead than I am.

"Since I mentioned my mother, we can begin my story with her—the narration which you asked for and which I believe is completely useless. My mother was a saint who was very eager to do good. Like a Sister of Charity she spent her nights without sleeping a wink, caring for the sick. She took the bread from our mouths to give to those poorer than we were. For shrouding and laying out the dead, her hands were like silk. And the day I was born, there was another child in the neighborhood who had been left without a mother so mine gave him her full breasts. This stranger grew strong and robust and I was left weak and sickly because there wasn't enough milk for the two of us. This was the first of the misfortunes which have been repeatedly my lot throughout all my life. I grew up and reached adulthood with my two brothers. But, since there wasn't enough money to pay the cost of professional education for the three of us, nor were there enough scholarships to go around, preference was given to the two older boys. So, it turned out that Joaquin went to the seminary and Francisco went to San Nicolas, the state university, because my mother had always wanted to have a priest and a lawyer in the family: one to keep us in good graces above and the other to defend us down below. For me, my parents chose

13

an office that would share a bit of each of the other two professions. They made me an altar boy in the local church. In this way, I would wear a cassock like a priest and I would handle money like a lawyer. Acolytes, you know, are like executors for the saints since all the money that is collected during holy services passes through their hands. I was very adept, very correct in my ecclesiastical responsibilities. I was also very respectful to the priests. I never turned my back, irreverently, on the altar on which the sacrament of Our Lord was exposed. I never threw pepper into the incense burner just to make the celebrant of the Mass and the nearby worshipers cry. Neither did I take leaks in the corners of the Sacristy like the other altar boys did.

"At meal time, the people used to see me go by, headed for my house, dressed in my red cassock, and they began to talk quite excitedly:

"Ah, what a good boy is Conchita Gaona's son— so pious, and so very serious!'

"And do you know why I never took off my cassock until I got home? Well, I didn't have any pants to put on and with the long skirt of the cassock I was able to cover my nudity all the way down to my ankles. This way, I discovered that religious habits hide many things which in the light of day cannot be exposed.

"One character, Melquiades Ruiz, whose nickname was St. Dismas, was a fellow-acolyte and, in addition, my adviser and instructor in deception, trickery, and mischief in general.

"First, he taught me how to smoke, inside the church, and then, how to drink the holy wine from the cruets used in Mass. He was called St. Dismas, not because he was a devotee of The Good Thief, but rather because he was such a good thief himself. This sly character used to spend his time burning my rump with the hot coals from the incense burner. When I protested, he would say to me:

" 'Brother Pito, pain is a penance and therefore your burns are bringing you much closer to Our Lord. I am only Divine Justice, who punishes your weak side.'

" 'But look! That's my strong side you're burning, you silly bastard!'

"Once, we saw a wealthy farmer from Turiran who, after praying for quite a while, dropped a silver coin in the Poor Box that was there in front of the painting of *The Apprehension of Christ* on the Mount of Olives. He did this as an act of thanks because there had been no freezing weather in his desert-like hot lands.

" 'Look, Pito,' St. Dismas said to me, 'How fortunate is the painting of *The Apprehension of Christ* and with what little concern He receives the gifts of the faithful, which will be used later by the good father for his own personal welfare. You have already heard that he wants to go to Morelia to buy a high-winged chair with whatever is collected. What do you think about getting up real early and beating him to the collection box?'

"St. Dismas convinced me without too much trouble. Because he was older than I and because of his popeyes, which had a certain saintly look about them, he had a certain power over me. Add to this the fact that my ideas about private ownership of property never were very rigid, and even less strict when it was a question of these earthly possessions which belonged to the saints whom I had always imagined were very, very considerate with the poor and needy and, besides, they had no recognized legal means with which to prosecute anyone in the state courts."

"And your conscience, Pito Perez?"

"I keep it well hidden in my cubbyhole of useless stuff.

"The following morning the two of us arrived at the church just before dawn. While St. Dismas lighted the candles on the high altar for the first Mass of the day, and watched carefully the door to the Sacristy, I tiptoed to the painting of *The Apprehension of Christ*. Having come prepared, I took a knife with a broken tip out of my cassock. I pried open the lid of the collection box. Slowly and fearfully, I put both hands inside. There, among all the copper coins, were some silver ones which opened their big eyes, frightened, like young, nude maidens surprised by a band of muggers.

" 'Sh,' whispered St. Dismas from the high altar when he heard the coins clinking together. At this, I got so scared that I imagined I had seen the painting of Our Lord stretch out his arm as if he were trying to grab me. I quickly put all the money in my red neckerchief and, trembling all over, I gave it all to St. Dismas who fled the church like some lost soul being carried off by the Devil.

"Just then Nazario, the sacristan, came in and he said to me: 'Pito, get a move on. Father is already getting dressed for Mass.'

"I walked toward the Sacristy, all the while watching the first women now coming into the church and getting themselves settled on the small benches of the confessionals in order to confess their sins of the night before.

"Father Rapper was putting on his religious garb. The only thing left to put on was the black chasuble, with its gold braid, used in the Mass of the Dead.

"We altar boys called him Father Rapper because of his rather easily irritated character and because of his habit of rapping us continuously on our poor heads with his fingers which were as yellow and as knotted as stalks of bamboo.

"We then left the Sacristy together, to celebrate the Mass. Father walked with his eyes lowered, but nothing escaped his penetrating scrutiny and, as altar boy, I followed with the Missal held very devoutly against my breast and my ears cocked in every direction, trying to find out if the theft had been discovered. Father Rapper looked like a big capital letter, in gold, and I—an insignificant small one printed in red ink.

"Mulling over my crime, I completely forgot the responses of the Mass, and to keep Father from finding out, I answered with some gobbledygook as incomprehensible as the Latin used by some of these priests who talk a lot but really say very little. When the Missal was rearranged for the final prayers, I cast a sideward glance at the painting of Christ and I also noticed that the sacristan was speaking in a very heated manner, completely surrounded by a group of parishioners, those devout women who had been at Mass and who, in turn, were attentively eyeing the empty Poor Box. Dawn, with its cowardly light, had revealed the theft and when we entered the Sacristy, Nazario came to meet us. Very excitedly, as if he were announcing the arrival of an earthquake, he said, 'They have robbed the Poor Box!'

" 'What are you saying, Nazario? Have they taken the holy painting of *The Apprehension of Christ?*'

" 'No, Father. But they did take the holy cash from His box!'

" 'Where is St. Dismas?' Father Rapper shouted,

clamping his eyes on me as if he were trying to penetrate my thoughts. Rapidly removing his religious belt and his stole, he shoved me violently into a corner of the Sacristy.

" 'Pito Perez! Get down on your knees! Pray for forgiveness and then confess: Who stole Our Saviour's money?'

" 'I don't know, Father.'

" 'HIC ET NUNC I shall condemn you to Hell if you don't tell me who the thief is.'

" 'It was I, Father!' I exclaimed in anguish, frightened beyond description by those Latin words I didn't understand and which therefore seemed very formidable to me.

"With his wirelike fingers, the priest grabbed one of my ears, almost tearing it from my head. Shaking me furiously, he shouted, 'Get out of here, you Pharisee, you evil, vile person; Pito, you, you disgusting person. If you don't want to be burned in the fiery depths of Hell, give me back the money, and now!'

"When Father Rapper loosened his hold a little, I ran. And I didn't stop until I reached home. I didn't see St. Dismas again. He kept all the money which I had taken from the Poor Box and the whole town soon learned of our theft because Father Rapper took it upon himself to spread the word from his pulpit. 'Two traitorous Judases have stolen from the Church. Out of charity, I shall not give their names,

19

but one is known as St. Dismas and the other is called Pito Perez.'

"The people made up some verses about us, some very badly worded verses, but with a still worse intention:

> To Dismas, Gestas did shout:
> "This kind of bullshit is out!"
> And to Pito, Dismas did reveal:
> "I'll screw you up right if you squeal."

> The alms of all the faithful flocks,
> That lay so still in the holy box,
> That belonged to The Apprehension of Christ,
> Were the object of a mysterious heist.

"The saddest part of the entire matter was that St. Dismas was able to become a member of the parish again, rehabilitated by my confession. He had his cake and ate it too, as the saying goes, and I on the other hand, I was the one who lost face. And the only memento which I salvaged from my life as an altar boy was the red cassock, spattered with wax and full of burn-holes put there by the sparks from the incense burner."

"Pito Perez, nobody knows for whom he works; this St. Dismas must have thought that the thief who robs a thief gets a hundred years of pardon, and, he who seeks too much wool gets clipped himself."

20

"Don't give me any more sayings. Everyone of them could serve as a title for the various chapters of my life. Now, I'm leaving. My whistle is dry. Let's have that bottle you promised. I think I've earned it today."

W hy do they call you *Pito?* Believe me when
I say that I have never learned why."

"This nickname really does not imply the vulgarity some people associate with the word and you shall
know how the name came about. Like all poor children, I never had any expensive toys nor pretentious
amusements. My mother always kept me under her
thumb. She never let me out in the streets for fear
that I would get lost. Lost, that is, in the broadest
sense of the word. Oh, if that poor woman were to
see me now! Anyway, confined as I was to the yard
of my house, I spent the time arguing with my sisters
or making little earthen ovens in which I baked my

mud pies. Quite skillfully, I kneaded bread, sprinkled on top with grains of sand to resemble salt. And I made sweet rolls out of mud. I also made dumplings stuffed with horseshit, which I forced my sister Concha to eat by threatening to tell our mother of certain amorous goings-on between her and the son of Zenon, the deaf man in town.

"During those long periods with really nothing to do, I used to whittle with a razor, and out of a piece of bamboo I carved a small flute, a *pito* as we say around here. By means of patience and spit, I finally learned how to get a few discordant notes out of my *pito* and later, after a lot of practice, a few tunes which were then popular in our area.

"The neighbors became quite exasperated listening to my long concerts of tremolos, arpeggios, lengthy cadenzas, and trills. They had *pito* when they got up, *pito* when they ate, *pito* when they went to bed. Finally, they had so much that they rose in protest and begged for mercy.

" 'Herlinda, shut that *pito* up!'

" 'Keep that *pito* quiet!'

"And *Pito* became my nickname—and I have never had cause to be embarrassed by this word.

"After my escapade with the money that belonged to the painting of *The Apprehension of Christ*, I devoted all my zeal and energy to my little flute. This was necessary because my mother, who had been seriously shamed by Father Rapper's pronouncement, had absolutely forbidden me to leave the yard.

"So, seated like a snake charmer on the edge of the base of the well, I spent my time making my sad and weary thoughts dance to the rhythms of my music. But the day came when, fed up with that prison in which I existed, I made up my mind to run away. So, at dusk one Thursday, after telling my family that I was going to church to pray, I started out.

"Without even a change of clothes, without a hat, without any plans for the future, with a total capital of ten cents in my pocket, I set out, hell-bent for election, on the Tenerias' road that leads to Cerrito, up in the hills. When I reached Cerrito I stopped to take my bearings and to make sure that no one was following me.

"The village down below stretched out its white streets to me, as if it longed to have me back in its loving arms. But, the road with all its mysteries drew me on.

" 'Farewell, Santa Clara del Cobre, village which saw me born, village which reared me a sad and humble child. I shall return—a conqueror—and then your great bells shall peal out to receive me!' "

"And where did you finally stop, Pito Perez?"

"In Tecario, at dawn the following day, tired, hungry, and cold. I made my way to the town square where I looked for something to eat and a place to get warm. Seeing me walk through the streets so early in the morning, without a hat, the people probably figured I was from some nearby farm.

"In a small doorway some women were selling cups of coffee filled with orange tree leaves which had been dipped in aguardiente. The first cup that I drank brought me back to life and the second made me forget that I was running away from home. It fortified my spirits and enabled me to continue on my way like the discoverer of a new world. Scarcely a few miles separated me from my hometown and already I thought that I had accomplished a deed worthy of the greatest conquerors: Julius Caesar + Hernando Cortes = Pito Perez. Most of my capital gave out when I bought the third cup of coffee, but my fanciful imagination had been lighted up brightly.

"From the bench on which I sat I saw a large, well-stocked store, perhaps the best in town. Even at this early hour of the morning, it was already filled with customers. Two or three clerks, in their shirt-sleeves, were waiting on the people and a bald, old man, without doubt the owner, was hunched over a desk, like a big metal hook. He was completely absorbed in the work he was doing on the account books. High up on the shelves, all neatly piled in rows, there were large squares of solid, lump sugar, each wrapped in blue paper and each proudly showing its factory trademark: *Cahulote Ranch*.

"Suddenly an idea came to me: By hook or crook,

25

get one of those delicious squares! I went into the store and going over to one of the clerks, I asked for a penny stick of cinnamon. This was the only coin which I had left!

"When I had the stick of cinnamon in my hand, I went over to the store owner. Showing him my purchase and putting on the look of a whipped dog, I asked him for a little square of sugar, a lump of sugar, if you will."

" 'OK. Tell them to give you one,' the old man answered. I scurried to the other end of the counter and, in a very affirmative tone of voice, announced: 'The boss says for you to give me a square of sugar.' I pointed to one of the large squares that was there near the ceiling. The clerk, a little uncertain, shouted to his boss: 'Shall I give this boy one of these squares of sugar?'

"The old man answered affirmatively without lifting his eyes from his work, assuming that it was a question of only a small lump of sugar to help sweeten a cup of cinnamon tea.

"The clerk took the square of sugar down from the shelf and I left carrying it in my arms, caressing it affectionately. I hightailed it away from the store as quickly as possible.

"This was both my first conquest of stupid people and my first entry into the world of drunks because the coffee I had drunk, loaded as it was with aguardiente, made me feel as if the sun in all its glory was burning inside me. From that moment on, out of my mouth would come the spirit, the spirit of wine. And like the prophets of olden days, I would spend the rest of my life in a state of total illumination, or if you wish, all lit-up."

"You complain about your bad luck. But, nevertheless, the theft of the square of sugar didn't turn out badly."

"That was no theft! To the contrary! It was a loan, obtained with God's permission! I never lay my hands on anything which belongs to someone else without first offering a mental request to the Supreme Creator of all things who is, therefore, absolute owner and master of all that exists. If the Lord agrees to my request, He permits me to take what I need. If He doesn't agree, He alerts the temporary owner who prevents me from achieving my ends in any way he chooses."

"Pito Perez! You are really great!"

"Ingrate you really should say, because I live and drink in great style. But, I don't have too much confidence in my system because I know full well that what life gives with one hand, it takes away with the other.

"Anyway, I sold the square of sugar in some run-down store outside Tecario and then I kept right on going. I was afraid some policeman might make that sweet deal bitter with his presence.

"With my *pito* in my mouth, I traveled along

the roads, the byways, and the paths in the hills, dreaming that I would teach the birds how to sing. Huh! What folly! The birds flew away, frightened when they heard the harsh notes coming from my flute. And, as a protest, they let loose their sweet trills when they were high in the branches of all the trees.

"What do the birds sing? What divine melody without words? What melody capable of stirring even the battered spirit of a drunkard? 'Wait, my little traveler,' I would say to a cautious little creature, watching it hide itself high in the top of some gigantic pine tree. Wait, for I am going to play the 'Miserere' from *Il Trovatore,* a selection I learned from Hilario, the church organist who played it while His Holiness raised the Host at Mass! But the bird warbled his own *Ninth Symphony,* then flew away without paying the slightest attention to me.

"Slowly but surely I made my way to Urapa. In this one-horse town located in the hot country, I applied for a job as a pharmacist's helper.

" 'What is your name, young man?' the druggist asked me.

" 'Jesus Perez Gaona, at your service, if we can get together on terms.'

" 'What can you do?'

"Remembering how I used to pick my nose, and without stretching the truth too far, I answered, 'I can make pills.'

" 'And what else?' the druggist asked as he eyed me from head to toe.

" 'I can make foreign patented medicines.'

" 'Well, I'll try you for a few days,' the old man said. 'To see if you will really work out.'

"Thus, with the best of intentions, I went to work in the drugstore.

"The druggist was a man about fifty years old. His name was Jose de Jesus Jimenez and he weighed two hundred eighty-seven pounds, even after trying every reducing diet that had been recommended. He was so big that he barely fit inside the drugstore and when he walked, the flasks, the jugs, and the bottles rattled together as if shaken by an earthquake.

"He never left his house, not even to go to church, not even to attend the meetings of the city council. His laziness was so great as to be dangerous to his clients because in filling prescriptions, rather than expend the effort to get out of the big armchair which accommodated his hulk as if it had been made to his exact measurements, he could quite easily have substituted strychnine for quinine. Since he couldn't take pride in his body, which looked like a huge barrel without hoops, or in his face which had long since become a mass of blubber, he publicized, anywhere and anytime, the fact that he had studied for his profession in one of the finest schools in the world. And to this end, he had placed a sign squarely in the center of the entrance to his shop which was

29

called *The Pharmacy of Providence.* At the top of
the sign was a circle in which the attributes of medicine were described in allegorical form. Under the
circle, he had put the following, painted in gold letters:

J. de J. Jimenez
Ex-student of the School of Pharmacy
of
Guadalajara
Ex-Pharmacist in the Hospital
of
St. John of God
Ex-pupil of Dr. Prospero Lopez

"Some anonymous hand, working in the darkness
of night, had written below the last of the statements
still another:

Ex-crement

"The name of the druggist's wife was Jovita
Jaramillo. Because of her initials, as well as those
of her husband, the townspeople called the drugstore *The Cemetery of the J's.*
"Jovita was a woman about forty years old. She
was thin and yellow, but with very correct features.
Her green eyes were in direct contrast with the color
of her skin and her chestnut-colored hair. In their
twelve years of marriage she had not had any children
and this state of affairs definitely had some bearing

30

on her becoming a very bitter woman. In fact, she had become so spiteful and complained so much that her husband never discussed any matter in her presence.

"On one occasion, I understand, a friend made some reference to my boss' great corpulence. And Jose de Jesus, lowering his eyes to look at his fantastic mountain of fat, sighed sadly and exclaimed, 'I haven't seen my little Jesus in ten years, not even in a mirror!'

"Doing eagerly whatever they wanted, I began to gain the confidence of the two people. To sustain his great laziness, the druggist used to sit in his big chair and while fanning himself with a newspaper, spend the days telling me what each of the numerous bottles contained and explaining the customary uses of these medications. He never ceased informing me that in filling prescriptions one should always use ingredients that are similar but less expensive than those indicated in the prescription: bicarbonate of soda instead of pricolite or sugar in place of antipyrine.

" 'Physicians prescribe some hard to find medicines,' he used to say, 'especially if they are not getting a kickback. But the official journal of our field helps us defend ourselves against their underhanded trickery, perhaps even to the benefit of humanity since, by altering the prescription, we kill fewer people. Here, just as you see me, by making up concoctions of simple, sweet syrup and by making pills out of starch, I have saved many lives and also a little cash on the side for my own welfare. Learn from me, Jesus. Follow my example diligently and your conscience will rest easy and you will also enjoy a full purse.'

"Following his advice, I began to concoct some really wild prescriptions and to take real pleasure in my job, like the chef who uses a little imagination when he seasons his dishes. In the drug business, when one has certain colorful inclinations, he can use certain harmless colorings which brighten up the eyes of the sick. Rosewater and currant oil, in proportions of one to two, for children who suffer from colic. Vegetable-green coloring converts pills into emeralds, and women, because of their attraction to jewels and jewelery, will gladly take them. But, what satisfied our customers most was the use of alcohol, in moderate quantities of course, stirred into the various medicines. After the first dose, the sick were cheered up. They sang, they slept well, and some escaped certain death, all of which honored and gave great fame to the physician who had treated them. Afterwards, according to rumors, they kept on taking the medicines to guard against any kind of illness. And, as if I had been struck by every disease in town, I began to test each and every one of those medicines, sampling them, tasting them just as a candy maker samples his own wares.

"Things went well for me in that job. I slept in the back of the shop on an old cot-like bed and I took care of the night calls so that Mr. J. de J's peaceful dreams would not be interrupted. The owners gave me the same food that they ate: for lunch, a large bowl of soup and one of rice, meat, and beans. Mr. J de J. was served double helpings of everything and he ate his soup by slurping it noisily from the bowl after seasoning it with at least fifteen different things: bananas, salt, lemon juice, peppers, pomegranate seeds, oregano, corn, avocado, pieces of tortilla, a dash of red wine, a few drops of oil, pieces of French bread, slices of hard-boiled egg, onions, and cooked potatoes. Every day, in front of the indifferent Jovita, who never ceased to complain about some imaginary illness, he prepared this complicated conglomeration with a superstitious expression on his face, much like that of a priest who celebrates some strange religious rite. And, the portions of those dishes he liked especially well were quadrupled. It's really a small wonder to figure out why the outhouse, which he visited so frequently, didn't overflow.

"In the store, I had within easy reach all the bottles of liquor and the cashbox which stood up well under my prudent filchings. For good reasons, the clerks in the other shops called any cashbox *Sir Prudence.*

"In addition to all this, Urapa was a small town with very few people. It would be difficult for any

33

inquiries of my whereabouts, which my beloved family might make, to get there. Thus, the town turned out to be a paradise for me and I didn't even have to mingle with all the animals of creation, each of whom was kept in his own house.

"But, there is no paradise without its temptations. When I told them that everybody at home had called me *Pito* Perez, by chance had I awakened those temptations that had lain dormant in that house? One afternoon, because of an association of ideas with my name, Jovita shouted from her room: 'Boy, bring some liniment!'

"With a holier-than-thou look on my face, I took a bottle of liniment to the room of the druggist's wife. She was stretched out in bed, face down, and she was groaning heavily. According to her, her side hurt, her back hurt, there were pains in her neck, and her aching body could not stand even the weight of a fly.

" 'It's my rheumatism acting up, pains shooting up and down my body. That's what makes me moan so,' she said with the voice of a spoiled child. 'But my husband is not the least concerned about my health and he never offers to give me a rubdown with anything. Oh! OHH! Ohhh! For pity's sake, rub a little liniment on my back.'

"And Jovita raised herself in order to loosen the fastenings of her blouse.

"My soul lit up with warm compassion for that

unfortunate woman who was suffering so much and, with virtuous intentions, I put my hand into the opening of her blouse and began to rub her bare shoulder ever so smoothly.

" 'That's it! That's it!' the suffering woman said in a most supplicating manner.

"Soon, she turned over and faced me. With her eyes closed, she whispered softly: 'Rub around my waist, and my chest, too, to stop these killing pains.'

"I did as she asked and as my hand moved upward, it touched two firm mounds whose peaks were quite rigid.

" 'That's it! That's it!' she repeated. And throwing her arms around my neck, she jerked me down on top of her aching body.

"Making a play-on-words, it soon changed from screaming to screwing.

"The effects of this medicine were surprising. Day after day, this suffering woman interrupted her pitiful moans to call to me from her room.

" 'Boy! Bring the liniment!'

"And, day after day, I got the bottle of liniment from the shelf and hurried to fulfill my mission of mercy.

"While all this went on, Mr. J. de J. remained in the front part of the drugstore, immovable in his big armchair. However, one day, one of those days when everything goes wrong, one of those days which I should talk about in whispered tones, three demanding customers came into the store at the same time. The druggist, with almost superhuman effort, got up from his chair and came to the back of the house to look for me. He pushed open the bedroom door. When he saw what was going on, he stood there stunned. My fright was such that I got out of the bed like a sleepwalker and Jovita began to scream as if someone were scratching her to death with his fingernails.

"I ran from the room, tripping over the furniture while the druggist, coming out of his stupor, began with great eloquence to call his wife such names as *whore, ungrateful bitch,* and *contributor to the delinquency of minors.*

"Without even stopping to gather my few belongings, I ran from the house and through the yard gate, so afraid of the anger of that furious husband that I decided immediately to get out of town, but quick. And, if it had been possible, I would have gotten off of this world, provided I didn't lose my life.

"That night, traveling my lonesome way, I thought sadly: 'How short are the pleasures of this world and how easily we let ourselves be overcome by temptations.' Again homeless and penniless, I was on the adventure trail all because I had forgotten the story of Potiphar's wife.

"My weariness made me recall my unhurried and easy life in the druggist's home: the wonderful food, the drinks of altered medicine, and the frequent filches from the cashbox. All lost, gone completely, because of Jovita's unsuspected passions."

"You are more of a poet than I, Pito Perez. And, after your affair with the druggist's wife, where did you end up?"

"I'll tell you tomorrow. Right now, I must have a few drinks, to console these sorrows which we have awakened. To speak of my past is to bring a dead man back to life and I can only talk about the dead when I am drunk."

I started out for La Huacana, taking a round-about way in order to avoid the San Pedro Jorullo property, a ranch which was owned by some fellow-townsmen from Santa Clara del Cobre. I was very desirous of avoiding them because if they learned that I was in the neighborhood they certainly would have gotten the information to my family.

"Because I had not grown up in a great metro-politan area, I have always preferred small towns to large cities which really are nurseries for the vain and hiding places for rare and odd goings-on. City dwellers can be classified as follows: a few families with extensive land holdings which were inherited, or which they acquired by means of some shady deal; a few elaborate but run-down houses whose closets are stuffed with documents which state that a great-grandfather was a judge on the Supreme Court or another was a colonel in the Revolutionary army or that another was the brother-in-law of the Count of Fat Hill or a nephew of the Marquis of Sierra Madre. These persons set the tone for the *high-society* gatherings at which there always appear the earrings which Empress Carlota gave someone or the lace shawl which someone's grandmother wore when she was a bridesmaid at the wedding of Señora Doña Lorenza Negrete Cortina de Sanchez Tagle These are very conceited people who make themselves look ridiculous everywhere by putting on the dog—like the time they invited Maximilian to visit Morelia, the capital of Michoacan. One of the leading citizens of the city putting on his most royal airs, asked the Emperor: 'And how is dear little Carlota?'

"The Emperor, very proper and very circumspect, answered: 'Her Majesty, the Empress, enjoys splendid health.'

"And the Emperor declined the invitation of those persons who were so completely unaware of accepted protocol.

"The families of government employees come next after this race of snobs, then the families of the professionals, then those involved with the clergy, and finally, that anonymous mass of humble laborers who barely have enough to eat and whose daughters are so crude that they make overtures when some rich bastard showers them with little favors. Why do they do this? What is the precedent for this action? I don't know. You figure it out! You are a pretty good figure-outer.

"In those big cities, misery and poverty take on many tragic faces and shameless no-goods like myself can't live there in any creditable manner. On the other hand, small towns are to my liking. In them, man and all of nature, nature in its broadest sense, blend together. Either that, or I'm confusing nature with man.

"But, it is indeed a fact that I love life in the flea-bitten, small towns. I love them because in them I'm a somebody, a person catered to by the simple folk who are honored to have me as a friend and who are entertained by my stories. I have sat for days at the table of a wealthy farmer and I kept him completely spellbound with my lies and he, when he heard them, never stopped asking: 'And what happened then, Mr. Perez? What happened next, Sir Pito?' Just like a small child when he listens to fairy tales!

"I carried on until my fountain of inspiration went dry. Then, I had to renounce his hospitality, paid for by the talents of my fanciful imagination.

"In these small towns the rich man is a farmer and the poor man is a laborer, which really are one and the same thing. The only exceptions are Mr. So and So, the merchant, who robs them both and Mr. Who's It, the druggist, who cleans them all out: sometimes their stomachs, sometimes their livers, but always their pocketbooks.

"At dusk, the laborer comes in from the fields, completely done-in from plowing all day, longing for a little pleasant conversation. So he goes to the tavern of his good friend, Gumersindo. There, as if by chance, is Pito Perez! And they offer him a drink, hoping that he will liven up the place. So Pito Perez comments on the news which the papers have printed. He repeats all the good things he has heard about those present, being very careful not to use any word which might cause his listeners to be less generous with their drinks. And so, offered a drink by this fellow and another by that fellow, Pito Perez soon has his belly full of drink and a sandwich which the bartender has given him on the sly, simply because Pito flatters him too. Oh, those wonderful small towns! Shangri-la for the lazy and Paradise for us windy boys!"

"But don't digress so much, Pito. Tell me what you did when you got to La Huacana."

"I sat down on a bench in the town square, under some tamarind trees which were so filled with blossoms that they looked like one of those canopies which were used to protect foot-travelers of old when

41

they trod their way along the roads. And this one seemed to be a new one, unfolded for the first time above the head of a traveler.

"The bells of the parish church were calling the people to Mass and a number of persons made their way sanctimoniously to the services. Then, my thoughts turned to God, as do the thoughts of everyone when he needs something. 'Let's test,' I said to myself, 'what kind of generosity the people of La Huacana have.' And then I sauntered slowly through the marketplace to see if the Lord would place something to eat within easy reach.

"After going up and down the streets, all to no avail, I went into the church and sat down in front of a confessional in which a priest was listening to the hushed confession of one of those religious old biddies. When I saw the dark, pockmarked face of this Messenger of the Lord, I recognized the man immediately. It was Father Pureco, from Santa Clara del Cobre, a priest whom I had served at Mass quite often. I couldn't hold myself back and I got close enough to the confessional to hear the worthless advice that he was giving to the woman who was confessing: 'Love your husband as the Church loves Christ; A woman should always remain silent; Don't argue with your husband even if he is as you say he is—more stupid than you. Now, put your offering in the box and go in peace, my daughter.'

"He gave her absolution and turning to me, he said, 'Pray the Confiteor.'

" 'I am Jesus Perez.'

" 'That isn't the Confiteor and I don't even know you.'

" 'Yes, Father, you do know me. I am Pito Perez, from Santa Clara.'

" 'You are Pito Perez?' the priest exclaimed in a tone which seemed to me to be a joyous one.

" 'The one and only Pito, Father, but dying of hunger.'

" 'Go to the Sacristy. Wait for me there. I want you to tell me everything that has happened to you.'

"In Santa Clara, Father Pureco was always considered somewhat dense and slow-witted. And, may God forgive me if, in saying this, I speak badly of one of His representatives, although without doubt the Holy Ghost is well aware of the talents of His Cabinet members.

"When Father came to the Sacristy, I related a most pathetic tale, telling him how the poverty of my family had forced me to leave Santa Clara in search of work. I told him about my perseverance in securing funds with which to help my sisters. And my hunger put such a moving tone to my voice that Father Pureco, as a first act of benevolence, offered me asylum in his house. Throwing his cloak around his shoulders, he took me there and gave me a pitcher

43

of milk and some bananas which had been fixed the way they like them in the hot country.

"At lunch time, Father plied me with questions about the fate and fortune of all the people in Santa Clara. I satisfied his curiosity as best I could, garnishing each account with details of my own making. This action almost caused me to lose my generous host.

" 'And Marin Pureco? What is he doing?'

" 'Nothing, Father, because he has passed on to a better life.'

" 'What! He's dead?'

"Father was on the brink of fainting dead away. The person he had inquired about was his brother and I hadn't known it. I had to bring this *dead man* back to life immediately and, with my talent for using words, make Father forget the false death notice.

"In the days that followed I helped Father Pureco with all his duties in the church. I collected all the offerings without taking my cut. I changed the clothes of all the holy statues. And because there was no organist, I filled the corners of the church with music from my prodigious flute. The faithful were quite surprised at this unexpected music, but from the choir loft I noticed that when I played some lively dance tune, they were immediately cheered up and kept time with their heads.

"During High Mass, on the Sunday following my

arrival, when the attendance by the farmers of the area was high, Father Pureco mounted his pulpit to preach his sermon. First, he said an *Ave Maria* as a means of asking the Virgin for inspiration. Then he cleared his throat, adjusted his false teeth, and let fly with the full force of his verbal eloquence.

" 'On other occasions, from this sacred spot, I have explained to thee, my brethren, the theological virtues. But, thee have heard me with indifference, much like one who hears the rain fall, but never gets wet. Indeed, the theological virtues are too few in number for thee not to know them well. But, forgive me, my God, He who is Supreme and Transubstantiated,' he said as he turned and faced the High Altar, 'I have a flock of dimwits who do not understand Christian doctrine. Once more will I explain what Faith is, what Hope is, and what Charity is.

" 'What is Faith? Be moved, ye hearts of stone. Faith is a white dove which we carry hidden in our tender breasts. But, we must awaken this dove so that she may lead us to the Gates of Glory. And, to awaken her, we must first cast forth from our breasts the hawk of sin, for if we let that hawk reside within, he will ultimately devour the innocent little dove.

" 'And Hope? Can there be anything more beautiful than Hope? Only the Holy Virgin Mary is more beautiful than Hope. And what is Hope? Listen carefully and engrave my words in thy hearts. Hope is the second theological virtue. Oh, how sweet it is to repeat with our Lord: "What hope I have to mend my evil ways, to cleanse my conscience, and to come to know my God." Even when it is a question of material things, how rewarding it is to have Hope! Because, provided our thoughts are in God, it is not sinful to say: "I hope to have a house, a wife, and many children, which really are the fruits of such a holy union; I hope to win first prize in the lottery. I hope that on my birthday the faithful will buy me a new cassock and a watch which I need so much.

" 'And Charity? The word itself reveals its real meaning. Giving! Giving! Giving! For good reason it is the greatest and the most powerful of the virtues. But what do ye understand of divine maters, regardless of how much the Holy Ghost inspires my words? My only desire is to light up the dark clouds of your understanding with the unfailing light of Truth! Oh, but with Thy permission, oh Transubstantiated Sovereign Lord, all of you, you are a bunch of stupid jackasses. No! I cannot retract what I have just said. Not until ye have shown that Faith exists within ye, that thy Hope is alive, and ye manifest thy Charity with deeds. Ye know that my birthday is August 24th! . . . Go in peace. In the name of the Father, of the Son, and of the Holy Ghost. Amen.'

"Father Pureco came down from the pulpit filled with the fire of inspiration. He was unaware that his gown had gotten hung up on a nail in the door. Unaware, that is, until he heard it tear. And, without asking permission of the Transubstantiated Sovereign Lord, he let loose with an 'Oh, shit!' that was as sonorous as a full slap in the face.

"We went home and at dinner time, as though he did not wish to bring up the subject, Father Pureco asked me: 'What did you think of my sermon, Pito?'

" 'Very good, Father, especially that line about *our tender breasts*. But it lacked that one essential which is necessary to stir the faithful: Latin. Really, Latin is the one thing that will make pious worshipers cry in church.'

" 'That's true, Pito. But I don't remember any of the Latin phrases of the Holy Fathers.'

" 'I can help you there, and in many other ways too, Father,' I said, desirous of winning him over. 'You will see. I will give you some Latin phrases; you will learn them and then, without asking permission of the Transubstantiated Lord, belt them out in your sermons in place of those harsh words you used today.'

" 'I'll tell you why I use those ugly words,' he answered. 'I only preach that way on Sundays, because that is the day the farmers come to hear Mass and they don't understand any other kind of language.'

" 'Ah, Father, that's where you're wrong. They *should* not understand you because you want them

47

to think of you as a wise man. Physicians, when they are with their patients, use the scientific names for illnesses and diseases. If they used the common names, the patients would understand them and cure themselves with tea and warm bricks.'

"I convinced Father Pureco that I was right. Then, I set to work looking for phrases in Latin. I found a dictionary which contained some expressions in that language, but because I wanted to make myself completely indispensable, I covered the book with a newspaper so that the priest wouldn't find out how I had acquired so much learning. On small slips of paper I copied down words which in my judgment could be used—small scraps of paper which Father Pureco then slipped out of his breviary when he was in the pulpit. He picked them out much like those trained birds at county fairs who, with their beaks, pick a piece of paper from among many that are in their cages and on which one's fortune is written. When he would see me reading on the sly, he always thought that what I had was some pornographic novel and he reprimanded me harshly, but always with a devilish, sly smile on his lips.

"Not very certain of what he was saying and fearful of offending God, Father Pureco, before he pronounced any of the Latin words which I had given him, always said: 'With Thy permission, Sovereign and Transubstantiated Lord.'

" 'Brothers in Christ, thy ingratitude toward the

Divine Saviour pains me *ab ovo*. Come, kneel at His feet as the Gospels command: *bonum vinum laectificat cor hominis*. I want only thy salvation. On thy behalf I ask the mercy of the Supreme Judge and before Him, I wish to intercede and to say: "Lord, forgive them. Behold, they are here before You, repentant and *inpoculis*."

" 'Father, you got the slips of papers mixed up. You called the faithful ones drunkards,' I told him when he came down from the pulpit.

" 'It doesn't matter, Pito. I've called them worse things before and they never were offended.'

"I don't know if it was because of the Latin or if it was merely a coincidence, but it is a fact that the parishioners began to show a greater respect for their spiritual leader and he began to be more conceited and to take on airs, like any public bigwig. He went to such ends that he began to apply to me the Latin words I had taught him, and with greater skill than when he was in the pulpit. Before ordering me to do anything, he would say: *'Hoc volo, sic jubeo, sit pro ratione voluntas.'*

"Such dictatorial behavior, repugnant to my rebellious nature, plus the fact that I did not get any salary, plus the fact that I wanted to get drunk every once in a while—because in truth I had developed a real liking for the bottle and Father never let me so much as get a whiff of the stuff—all of these things made me think about leaving there to try my fortune

49

elsewhere. When a recurring fever hit me, I became convinced that I should leave La Huacana. This fever, during those periods when it was really rampant, made my entire body shake, almost as if I were being shaken in a sieve. After these seizures, I didn't even have strength to put food in my mouth.

"I decided then to leave Father Pureco, involved as he was in the ever-increasing entanglements of his Latin. So, as a remembrance of my stay, I took two or three of those *gold miracles* from the venerated statue of the Virgin of Solitude. But, much to my regret, I had to sell them out on the road. However, I can swear to the nonbelievers that I have manipulated my way through miracles and even have lived on them.

"I was really so tired and homesick that I no longer played my flute. I was completely obsessed with the idea of finding some way to get back home without being reprimanded or punished.

"I took two days to go from La Huacana to Ario de Rosales and two more from there to Santa Clara. I spent the nights high in the hills, weak from fever and fatigue—so much so that the stars looked to me like death candles that twinkled all around my dead body. I could have reached home when the sun was at high noon, but I thought it best to wait until nightfall so as not to attract attention in the streets. 'Surely,' I thought to myself, 'I will have to come before a family council. My sisters will scold me; my mother, Herlinda, will try to punish me. But afterwards, they will cry and when the storm is over, perhaps they will listen with some interest to the story of my travels. And they will end up by butchering a lamb to celebrate the return of the Prodigal Son.'

"So, seated on a rock on the side of the road, I waited for the afternoon to wear itself out. Then, like a beaten dog, I slowly made my way home and knocked at the door with more fright than shame.

"One of my sisters opened the door and as casually as if she had seen me leave a few minutes earlier, she said: 'Come in.'

"No one seemed the least surprised to see me. No one asked me where I had come from nor if I intended to stay. Rather, it was I who said to Concha, noting that she was preoccupied with something: 'You look so sad, Concha.'

" 'I am upset because last night I dreamed I laid an egg, a big one, and it took some doing. And I'm afraid this bad dream will come true!'

"Suddenly, it struck me that Concha looked like a mother hen, with glasses, and that everyone in our family had some animalistic characteristic: My mother had the face of a little puppy; Maria had the face of a gopher; Lola had the face of a wet bird; Joaquin that of an innocent rabbit and I, the face of a cunning rat.

"Nonsense caused by my fever! But, what kind of fever made Concha afraid of laying eggs?"

And did you get settled down again in your hometown?''

"Only for a little while, no more. To wander at will becomes quite a vice, and I will never give up my travels even if it's only a short journey, like from here to Opopeo. Just as the food in someone else's house seems to taste better, so the drinks in other towns have a more stimulating flavor, at least for us drunks.

"When I finally got back home, I soon learned that every night there was a kind of drinking contest for drunkards being held in Solorzano's place. A certain Jose Vasquez, jailer at the local drunk tank and a person whom I had never met, simply because he was somewhat of a newcomer in the town, was top man. Everybody said he was a real expert at bending his elbow at the bar, so much so that he left far behind all those who used to enjoy that fame and glory.

"My curiosity to meet this champion got the better of me. One evening I went to Solorzano's to wait for him. Vasquez arrived and asked the bartender to serve him something refreshing. Solorzano filled a large glass with aguardiente and Vasquez drank it down without stopping, just as if it were soda pop.

"They introduced me to him and when he heard the others in the tavern call me *Pito*, he thought that my nickname was an homey dimunitive of *Agapito*. So, with great courtesy and friendliness, and much to the amusement of the others there, he began to say: 'Sir Pito this' and 'Sir Pito that.'

" 'Sir, Mr. Pito, they say that you have traveled halfway around this world.'

" 'Of that territory included in the Bible, I know it all—except Sodom—Nineveh, Jerusalem, and Babylon. In this hemisphere I know Tecario, Ario de Rosales, La Huacana and many other towns whose names are so numerous I cannot remember them all. Little towns that are as big as ranches; ranches that are as big as cities!'

"Recalling that the owner of the tavern was a native of Patzcuaro and that he was listening to us very attentively, I then explained with great pomp and appropriate language: 'But the metropolis which I like best is Patzcuaro. Where else is there a city with a more poetic sadness? Where else a lake like that of Patzcuaro, liquid mineral whose stock of silver-colored fish is inexhaustible? Where else is there a view more beautiful than one sees from the top of Calvary Hill, a view which takes in all of Michoacan. And if we strain our eyes a little bit, we can even see the towers of the city of Guadalajara, a city unique in all the world because of the clearness of its air on the few days of the year when it doesn't rain? Where else is there a Virgin more miraculous than the Virgin of Health, the Virgin who grants whatever anyone asks her?'

" 'Isn't that true, Solorzano?' I asked the tavern owner, whose moustache was even trembling with pure emotion as he heard me exalt so fervently his home country.

"And then, I felt a diabolic plan developing in my mind.

" 'Look here, Mr. Vasquez. Let's ask the Virgin for a drink. If she really is so miraculous, she will provide what we ask for. I'm sure that the Virgin will not take a chance on standing in bad stead because of the little thing which we are going to ask her since a negative reply would really be a black mark against Patzcuaro.'

"I devoutly brought my hands together and lifted

my eyes toward the ceiling, as if praying. The arrow hit home, or rather it hit Solorzano's religious soft spot because he quickly set before each of us a glass full of the purest whiskey, which he had moonshined himself in the back part of that respectable business house, and which he had labled with the nationally known brand name of *Tancitaro*.

"The Virgin performed this miracle ten times in a row until finally, Vasquez was completely crocked and fell sound asleep on top of some large boxes. It was only with pure luck that I was able to get home myself.

"On a subsequent night, I tried again to awaken the civic pride of that mystical tavern keeper, but the Virgin did not repeat her miracles, perhaps because I did not pray for them with the faith necessary.

"At that time of my life, bad luck had as yet not unsteadied my nerves and I still had a round, clear, and beautiful handwriting. When Vasquez, the jailer, became aware of this he invited me to work for him as his secretary, a job which I accepted because I thought that since we were such good drinking companions, we would get along well working together. What a bunch of nonsense! Vasquez was one of those officials who takes advantage of his inferiors in every way he can, one who is never pleased with anything, and one who pawns off as his own the ideas of others. Whenever I spoke about the official matters of the jail, I always spoke my mind candidly and then later he always gave my opinions as if they were his own, and always with the same preamble: 'In my humble opinion . . .'

"In order to finalize my study of fools in general, I had only to become acquainted with the judge and his jailer. And now I know full well that what changes in man is the dimension of his work and that the fool or the person without a conscience is the same whether he is an official of a small town or a minister of state who resides in the capital of the country.

"In a government office one learns a great deal. People try to resist believing that public officials can be so very vain and that those who surround these officials can be so subservient and adulating.

"By the way, let me tell you a little story. A President of our country, a very good and democratic man, had a childhood friend who lived buried away in his small hometown, a man who never had asked the President for anything. But it happened one day that the friend, upon the advice of his local physician, had to go to the capital to be treated. Then, very naïvely, he said to himself: 'I will take advantage of this trip to stop by and greet the President and while I'm there I will ask this very generous man to help some of his old friends. Not for myself,' he continued, 'because thank God, I don't need anything.'

"After he had arrived in the capital, and when he had no appointment with his physician, he began to make calls on the Capitol Building and to become aware of the anguish that was so apparent in the anterooms. There, before the curious eyes of this country bumpkin, the ministers of state strolled by and the highest dignitaries of all the land came and went. Each, with a passing glance, eyed the poor souls seated there, those mortals who seemed like mushrooms born only to die in the dark corners of the anterooms. These persons scurried through these rooms with their briefcases under their arms, scarcely greeting each other under their breath. They opened the door to the presidential suite and were immediately lost in its mysterious depth. After several hours, these officials appeared again in the doorway, and with the same air of great importance. They again went through the anterooms, now surrounded by their clients and being flattered by their friends.

"After several days, the President learned that his friend from childhood, that quiet and reserved boy whom he had not seen in so many years, desired an audience with him.

" 'Have my friend come in,' he ordered the guard. And the friend came in, pleased and impressed to meet the President in the company of some of those proud and haughty gentlemen whom he had seen pass through the anterooms.

" 'Wait a minute,' the President said to him very kindly.

"The visitor sat down in a corner of the office,

waiting for that moment when the President would not be busy, so that they could relax and talk together of old times and recall memories of the old days gone by. But, with great surprise, he noted that the gentlemen who were present there in the room did not seem anything like those whom he had seen walk through the outer rooms. These men spoke in low voices with their heads bowed. They walked about on tiptoes and they went out of the office as if they were leaving the room of a very sick person.

"Finally the President was alone and turning to his friend, he said: 'Come on over. What are you doing here? How can I help you?' But the friend continued to stare at the door of the office, shaking his head sadly from side to side.

" 'What do you see?' asked the President.

" 'That door, that door which separates the real from the fraudulent, the door of pretenses, the door of changes. Before coming through that door, the high officials hide their rings, calm their gestures, restrain their ideas. And once out, on the other side of that door, they are other men, men who forget your doctrines and betray you in every way, even in the way they walk. On the other side of that door, they scorn all men; here inside, they don't have the guts to talk up to one lone man. Oh, pity the people! And tell me, sir, who is to blame, you or they?'

"The President thought that his friend had gone

crazy and he let him leave the room without lifting a hand to stop him.

"The story doesn't exactly fit here and I only mention it because I remember Vasquez and the judge who made me truly hate this world's justice with all its pitfalls and evils.

"Oh, pity the poor people! I advise them to respect the law, always, and to obey the law. But, I also advise them to piss on its representatives."

And what about love, Pito Perez? Has it been good or bad to you?"

"My friend, don't rub salt in the wound! Don't hit me where it hurts worst! Love is the incubator of all my bitterness; the mirror of all my disappointments. Love has worked against me in such a way that I am certain that if I could have found the stimulation to fight for something or for someone, today I would be a completely different man. They say that a woman has more power than a team of oxen. I believe it! But in my case, women have used that strength to get away from me rather than to get close to me. Here, just between us, I openly confess to you my vices which, in some respects, are no secret to anyone. Even though I am a drunkard and a kind of cheat, love could have made a different man of me. But Cupid, that impertinent little godlike creature, never came near me with any intentions of saving me, but rather to ridicule me. With his innocent, childlike hands, he broke all the strength of my will.

"So! Do I go through life dirty, disheveled, and unrestrained in my actions? So what difference does it make if I have no one who is concerned about me!

"So! I don't work? What difference does it make when I have no one to work for; when I have no one with whom to share my life!

"Who has ever taken a real interest in me? You yourself, the very person to whom I am telling my life story, have you ever really tried to know me, to study me with any real serious intent? No! You want me to tell you stories that will make you laugh: my adventures as a knave-like Periquillo; my tricks as a wandering rascal, like Gil Blas. But, have you ever noticed that my tricks are not funny ones? I do not have a generous spirit. Neither did I have a joyous childhood, one of those childhoods which, when the man reaches maturity, has him walking the straight and narrow path and preaching morality while he rocks his children's cradle. No! I will be rotten to the core until the very end. I will be a drunkard until the day I die, done in by alcohol. I will be envious of the good fortune of others because

I have never had any good fortune of my own. I will be vulgar because in vulgarity I find my revenge against those who look down upon me. And I will do nothing to change myself. Only cowards offer to make amends or to recant, and I will do neither. Humanity is a hypocrite which spends its life praising God, trying to deceive Him with the word Jesus on its lips and, at the same time, without any pity whatsoever, cursing and denying the Devil.

"Oh, the poor Devil. How sorry I am for him! He has never heard a single word of compassion or of love! Men are really insufferable bores. When they talk to God they do it with written formulas, one for each situation: 'Help us, O Lord. Give us this day our daily bread; Have mercy on us, O Lord!' To free themselves from pain they run to God, like they would to the dentist. But when they look for entertainment and pleasure, they have no shame when they seek out the Devil. And they plunge themselves into all of the delights of licentious living without ever once offering a single 'Thank you, my Devil!' To the contrary, because after they have tasted of his forbidden fruit, the Devil even has to listen to them give thanks to God for the pleasures they have had.

"I am not aware that Faust thanked the Devil for the youthful life, for the money, or for the love which the Devil gave him.

"The Devil moves about in shadowy circles, struggling continuously against hatred and envy, a stranger who is denied all affection, all expressions of tenderness.

"The Devil never knew a mother's warmth and Jesus was born of a virgin who was all purity, all love.

"The Devil may hate evil and love good, but he is not the master of his own free will. He was condemned to love hatred and to hate love, and he can never break with his destiny.

"Jesus Christ died but once, with all the sufferings of mortal man. But for time immemorial, the Devil will suffer his own tortures and those which Dante invented for him. Oh, the poor Devil What pity I feel for him!"

"Pito Perez, please excuse my interruption of your diabolical discourses, but I am very anxious to learn about your successes and your failures in this matter of love."

"Well, since you insist, I will tell you how often and in what way Love has made a fool of me. But don't expect to find idols entwined in moonbeams quoting poetry taken from some book of Lamartine or Victor Hugo. My loves were of the everyday type, crude, with little subtlety, and even vulgar. The greatest love I had was one in my childhood. But it died a secret, without the object of my affection ever really understanding my musical declarations.

"She lived across the street from my house and

her name was Irene. Irene! Her name was the prettiest thing about her. She was three or four years older than I; tall, slender, and her skin was the color of cinnamon. Her breasts were like two small pears which had been stolen and hidden under her blouse.

"Her family was quite poor, with very few possessions. Her father was a mule driver without any animals of his own and her mother ground chocolate which she sold to the grocery stores in town.

"Rather embarrassed, Irene used to knock at our door and ask if she could borrow a handful of salt or a little bit of sugar. Sometimes she was barefoot and seeing her feet and her bare legs, my first voluptuous thoughts were born.

"From our house, we could see the inside of theirs: two beds without mattresses, an unfinished table, and an old bench topped with broken flower pots through whose cracks flowers peeked, like the toes of little children, peeking through a wornout shoe.

"Every evening, at dusk, Irene came to her door and the flute of Pito Perez then poured out its song of love:

If you but knew my secret secret,
Of the love I bear in vain,
Then no more would you have cause
To hurt with such disdain.

" 'Now, yes now, she must have understood me,' I thought that night as I went to bed, picturing in my mind the two little pears of St. John that were hidden beneath her blouse and those bare feet that the rocks of the street treated so cruelly.

"It was one long year of passion, one year of musical concerts, one year of tender glances, without ever finding a way to say a single word to her. But vacation time came and my brothers came home: Joaquin, studying to be a priest and Francisco, studying to be a lawyer. And it was Francisco who turned out to be my rival because one night I surprised him as he was kissing Irene. And, I learned later that he had kissed her often on previous vacations.

"I ran out into the yard, sobbing over the death of my first love. My brother Joaquin followed me and said, 'Are you crying, Jesus? I know why! Cry it out, because tears can wash away the sorrows of love.' "

"And, Pito Perez, they say that music soothes the savage beast."

"Savage beasts, yes. But women are special kinds of doves whose hearts are protected by a shield of feathers which dull even the most venomous of arrows.

"What you have just heard is the schmaltzy chapter about my frustrated idyl. Now, let's get to the comedy itself where, amid all the laughter and joking, I failed again.

"I had an uncle who ran a store down on the town square. He wore a beard and moustache in the style of Napoleon III, and a top hat, and was more stupid than a goose. You will excuse me if I omit a certain other detail about this man's makeup.

"My mother spoke with my uncle about the possibility of my going to work as a clerk in his store. He finally gave in after lecturing me about honesty, insinuating that mine was somewhat questionable ever since that day I had stolen the money from the donation box in the church. And then he added some thoughts about the merits and the advantages of temperance. I went to work in the store resolved to be even more honest than St. Dismas, the real one that is, and not to drink any more than was necessary to keep my body incorruptible.

"My serious intent to be honest lasted only until that moment when I found out that the only salary that my uncle was going to pay me was my food. And not too much of that.

"The work was hard. He made me get out of bed at five o'clock in the morning and I literally fell back in it at eleven o'clock at night, whipped and exhausted. Insofar as my drinking was concerned, I arranged it so that I could drink all day long right under my uncle's eyes, assuring him that what I was taking was medicine which I had gotten at the drugstore. To corroborate my story, I wrapped the bottle in dark paper and glued on it the skull and crossbones that are usually used to show that something is poison. In order that the odor of the liquor wouldn't give me away, I mixed a few drops of essence of clove in with the aguardiente.

"I drank a bottle of this medicine daily, remembering how I had introduced this original therapeutic technique to the sick people of Urapa. By the time night had come, all of it had gone to my head. I saw the shop as a less gloomy place and I even began to pity the customers, so much so that I often tipped the scales in their favor. The real sharpies in the place saw this and they used to form a line to make their purchases just a few moments before *The Moorish Muse* closed. *The Moorish Muse* was the name of our store.

"My uncle had several daughters. Each was as different from the others as if they had had different fathers: tall and blond, dark and short. The one who had the darkest complexion was called Chucha. She looked like a devilish little monkey. Her face was covered all over with fuzz and she had small white teeth, like a rat.

"Chucha used to take advantage of the fact that her father took a siesta every afternoon. She would come to the store, smile at me coquettishly, go over to 'Sir Prudence' and take some money out of it. She said that this money was a contribution to the poor, but I was aware that Chucha was the best dressed of all my cousins and that she never was without a very colorful hairband.

"After our smiles had become habitual, conversations began and then came questions about the secrets of my life.

"Cupid struck again with one of his poisoned darts. But this time I was brave enough to confess it to the object of my passion, although it happened in a place not entirely suitable to such poetry, in the store's back room which smelled of tobacco and stale surplus goods which had been moved there from the front of the store.

"In a hushed and trembling voice I started my amorous advances:

" 'Come over here, Chucha. I love you.'

" 'I love you too, Pito.'

"One afternoon, as we hid behind a gunnysack filled with the husks of ground grain, I tried to kiss her. She turned her face quickly and my lips touched her ear, tickling her a little.

" 'Do you have a toothache, Jesus? You smell like essence of clove.'

She turned her mouth away from mine so quickly —I must have smelled like essence of drunkenness!

"My display of affection for Chucha and my sacrifices for her increased rapidly. I saved for her the newest coins that were put into the cash drawer; I bought a toothbrush; I reduced the spoonsful of alcohol to half-spoonsful; and I never again asked her to take care of the shop when I had to go to that certain distant and foul-smelling room in the house.

"Oh, wonderful love, so filled with self-denial!

"This lovesickness continued to grow and grow until it was converted into a serious danger, especially insofar as the economic stability of the business was concerned. I made a deal with Ruperto, who had quite a reputation as a good carpenter. He was to make me a wide, bounce-resistant wedding bed in exchange for some nails, glue, and other materials which he needed, all of which we carried in stock in the store.

" 'Why do you want such a strong bed?' he asked, curious. 'Are you going to marry Justina, that woman who works over in the restaurant? She weighs 275 pounds.'

"Really, I wanted a very wide bed in order to be able to sleep at a respectable distance from my wife-to-be so that she couldn't smell my breath which was scented up with tequila, mezcal, and all the other fine essences of the house.

"I used to say to Chucha, quite seriously, 'When are you going to give me your measurements so that I can have your wedding outfit made?'

"Night after night I planned on speaking to my uncle to inform him of my relations with his daughter and to ask his permission for a quick marriage. But whenever I was in his presence, I never had the courage because I was completely overcome by his moustache and beard which made him look like some old tintype picture. In view of the fact that the

69

days were hurrying by and that I did not have the courage to confront that well-knit trinity—my uncle, my boss, and my future father-in-law—I decided to commission a neighbor, Santiago, to go on my behalf and to ask for Chucha's hand in my name. This was the custom in our area. Santiago was a rich and respected bachelor and like the majority of the rich men in our town, he was bald and paunchy.

"Santiago listened attentively to my request and then repeated several times the name of the girl he was going to ask for. 'Chucha, isn't it, that high-spirited girl who sings a lot?'

"On the designated night, Santiago went to make the request that we had agreed upon. He was freshly bathed and clean-shaven and he carried in his right hand his cane with the horn handle. Because of the tensions that I was suffering, I forgot my resolutions against drinking and with my mouth glued to the bottle, I gulped down no less than a fifth of mezcal.

"As I strained my ears to hear what was going on in the other room, it seemed to me that the conversation was taking on an air of cordial understanding. Santiago's laughter and that of my uncle, hollow and cracked like that of some old actor, were heard all the way out in the front of the store. They called Chucha so that she might take part in that three-way conversation.

" 'Right now, they are probably asking her if she loves me.' I thought to myself as I suffered the pure pleasure that came with the thought. 'Now she is probably answering, timidly, that she does. Now, as is customary, her parents are probably saying, even though it may not be the truth, that they are giving her her freedom to choose a husband and they are reminding her that if she does not wish to go through with marriage, she will always have a place of her own in their home. Now they are probably deciding upon the proper time for the wedding.' And then, just as if reality were obeying my thoughts, I heard Santiago thanking them as he left and I saw my uncle, smiling and apparently satisfied, go into the store.

"'He's going to say something nice to me,' I thought, a little timidly. 'He's going to give me an affectionate embrace.' But he went straight to the dining room with a bottle in his hands, without saying a single word to me.

"After locking up the store, I went to look for Santiago. I found him seated in a chair made of cowhide, in the doorway of his house. He seemed very content as he smoked a cigar.

"'Did they agree, Santiago?'

"'They did, son, they did!'

"'And what arrangements were made for the wedding?'

"'None. And, I must tell you something, not really very important. I hope that you will not be too upset. Thinking on the matter, I realized that

you are too young to take on this kind of an obligation and so I asked for Chucha's hand for myself.'
And getting up out of the cowhide chair, Santiago
said goodnight to me, very cordially, and slammed
the door in my face. When I finally returned home
and got into bed, all of the bottles in the store were
trembling. They were afraid they were going to be
raped and the barrels thought that their final hour
had at last arrived. And then Bacchus took pity on
me and I fell asleep in his arms, just as if I had been
in the arms of a loving father.

"During the days that followed, Chucha became
quite a detached person, refusing to speak of this
unimportant matter. She would come into the store,
take the money from the cash drawer, then leave,
smiling as she used to do, showing her pretty white
teeth with the impish air of a little monkey.

"A few days after the marriage proposal, my uncle
told me that he was going to Morelia to take care of
some business and that I should stay there to take
charge of the store. Enjoying that freedom very
much, I used the money we took in to organize
dances on the outskirts of town. I also began to sell
merchandise on credit without recording any of the
sales so that I would not become addicted to the
greedy, petty habits of businessmen. God had
touched my heart and for the first time I was aware
of the pleasure to be had in being generous to those

who need help. The half-empty shelves in the store spoke highly of my generosity. I watched painlessly as those earthly goods disappeared, drunk either because of the godly art of giving or because of the liquor which I was consuming so devoutly and so abundantly.

"My uncle returned from his trip and when he saw the shelves stripped of their goods, he rubbed his hands together joyously.

" 'What happened to the merchandise? Based on what I see, you really sold a lot!'

" 'Everything has been sold, uncle.'

"My boss went straight to the cash drawer. When he found it empty, he asked with a certain uneasiness, 'Where is the money?'

" 'It petered out as I gave change, sir,' I answered sheepishly, trying to hide the matter of my good deeds because as the Bible says, 'Let not thy right hand know what thy left hand doeth.'

"My uncle was in no mood to accept the merit of my good conduct and, furious as a fire-eating dragon, with his moustache quivering with rage, he unjustly ran me out of his house. I left, *omnia mecum porto,* as Father Pureco might have said.

"From then on, I thought of Chucha as being dead. And today, when her memory plagues me too much, even though now she is the mother of many children, I dress myself in a ragged, black mourning

73

coat, put on a high silk hat, and go to the cemetery to take flowers to her, flowers which I lay on an imaginary tomb.

"I know that Chucha is upset when her lady friends tell her that Pito Perez is taking floral wreaths to her grave. So far as Santiago is concerned, he watches me go by, his eyes showing a certain sadness caused by envy, and he murmurs in a hushed voice: 'It's a pity that such a beautiful idea can't be the real thing!'

"So that you can be convinced once and for all that it is my destiny to be unhappy in love, I will tell you about my most recent escapade, which turned out to be a tragedy spattered with my own blood.

"Cliseria and her niece, Soledad, earned their living by selling corn in the front part of their house. At that time, the only work I had was that of studying my role as the hermit in Zorrilla's play *The Dagger of the Goth*, which was going to be staged in celebration of the birthday of one of the town's more important citizens. At rehearsal times, everybody chatted, laughed, drank, and told dirty jokes. Of course, I am indebted in part to that production for this terse and energetic voice which I have, because I took this role so seriously that all the events of my life became dramatic in character and lost all sense of reality. I remember that on the night of the production, Father Buitron whistled most beautifully an operatic selection and Jose Elguero recited some verses which he had written himself. But, let me get back to Soledad and her aunt, Cliseria.

"I have heard it said that there are some prize bulls which are given this name because they give a tremendous showing during every part of a bullfight. Cliseria was one of those bulls; she always came into the last minutes of any encounter with a man with a great surge of power, her two formidable horns poised, ready to do business.

"Soledad, the niece, inherited these talents from her aunt. She was a happy person, a flirtatious woman who spent her life strumming her guitar while a cigarette dangled from her mouth.

"When she would see me pass by in front of her house, she would shout to me with all her natural flippancy: 'Pito Perez, come here. I'll give you a drink and sing you a song if you'll give us an accounting of the corn we've sold this week.'

"I not only put their books in order, but just to keep Soledad playing and singing, I waited on the customers, one after another.

"When she crossed her legs she exposed most of herself, and when she lifted the guitar high on her chest her breasts stood up, rigidly, like another duet during an anxious moment in *La Traviata*.

"Finally, when I could withstand no longer the tormenting desire to know if those super-things were real or not, I put out my hand and placed it on Soledad's heart. Rather than interrupt the difficult piece she was playing, she did not draw back and my hand stayed where I had placed it.

" 'Be patient, Pito,' she whispered. 'I'll play you another song.' And with my hand on her heart, she played the second song—and everything was perfect. From that moment on, what a wonderful existence! No worries! No wants! Harmonious toccatas. Languid songs, romantic and sad, those songs that make one weep without knowing why! And because in this house they also fed me, I felt that suddenly I had become rich and that the grains of corn that were in those drawers were bright, shiny, gold coins; nuggets of old through which I ran my avaricious hands.

"But one day—oh what a day!—the guitar disappeared. Soledad did not come out of her room and Cliseria said to me with such frankness that I couldn't even give back the slightest answer: 'Don't come here anymore, Pito Perez. Soledad is going to marry the new tax collector. And he is jealous of you.'

"A proud man, and a gentleman, I didn't go back. In fact, I didn't even go down their street again.

"The wedding announcements were read and the day of the wedding arrived. From a distance, I followed the pair to the church and I saw them come out man and wife: she, without lifting her eyes from the ground, with all the modesty of an unexperienced beginner, and he, wiping the perspiration from his brow and puffing and snorting like a bull-ox harnessed to a wagon.

"Later, in the godfather's house, there was a lot of food and a little dancing. I decided to go to the celebration just to dine at least once at the expense of the husband, since I had dined so often before at the expense of the wife.

"The banquet was one of the best: from three kinds of soup all the way through to three kinds of dessert. And the guests were the most distinguished citizens of the town. Even Chucha was there with her venerable *San Diego* as the town gossips had now begun to call him.

"Hilario's orchestra played polkas and schottisches and Pedregoso's musicians played country music.

" 'Let's go, maestro. Let's have a waltz,' the people shouted to Pedregoso.

" 'I can't! I'm tuned up for a little more action than that.'

"Before the guests sat down at the table, they drank several glasses of Mexican purple passion, a mixture of wine, sherry, and other potent items.

"I sat down at the far end of the table, mixed in with the people of lesser importance, trying as best I could to hide the many worn spots in my suit.

"The time for the toasts rolled around. The first to speak was the priest, whose provocative smile and mellow character were the products of the ale he had

had to drink. 'Grow and multiply, my children,' he said.

"After that, the secretary of the town council spoke. He praised the splendid youth of the husband and the innocence of this virgin who had dressed herself in the traditional wedding-white. When the secretary finished, I stood up and improvised these rather poor verses:

> *And for the wife which you now boast,*
> *The townfolks drink a friendly toast.*
> *She's kind and pretty, and generous too.*
> *Oh yes, I forgot—she's almost new.*
>
> *Upon her breast is a beauty mark,*
> *And there's fuzz on the calves of her legs.*
> *And you'll be happy and glad to know*
> *For a touch on some spots she just begs.*
>
> *When kissing and hugging and other such stuff,*
> *She bites and she scratches and boy, does she rave!*
> *And oh, how awful her armpits smell*
> *When after such action she does not bathe.*

"The husband leaped to his feet, his hair literally standing on end and his eyes flashing mad. He grabbed a bottle from one of the tables and threw it at me with such dead aim that it hit me squarely in the face and sent me reeling across the floor, bathed in my very own blood.

"The dinner guests scurried away from the table

and the musicians hurried into the room to play their music. In the middle of all of this uproar, as I later was told, only San Diego was laughing— thinking, and perhaps rightly so, that he, on his wedding day, had escaped a toast which would have been in much the same vein.

"My luck as a lover has been all bad. Recalling all of my misfortunes, I am reminded of these very well-known verses which, I must say, really do not synthesize my life right down to the letter:

What favors to the sun do I owe,
For having kept me warm?
If, as a child, I went to school;
If, as a husband, an ignorant fool;
If, when alive, a fighting man;
If, when dead, completely damned.
What favors to the sun do I owe,
For having kept me warm?"

One rather indiscreet question, Pito Perez. Is it true that you know many jails firsthand?"

"Yep, it's true. I know quite a few from personal experience, and I'm not ashamed to confess this publicly. I have spent a lot of time in them, locked up for being drunk or as a public nuisance. But I have never killed anyone, nor have I committed any of those crimes for which the rich are commended and the poor are sentenced to many years in prison. A rich man kills and then he takes refuge in his hideaway while his money greases palms and buys off the law. A rich man can commit a crime and gather such convincing evidence of his innocence that when the whole matter is aired in public it appears that he is the one who has been slandered and that he is the real victim of the crime.

"I have never had the good fortune to be sentenced to one of those modern jails, one of those jails where, according to what I have heard, everything is comfort and refined customs; one of those jails where the prisoners wear those elegantly styled uniforms which have become so much the fashion outside of penitentiaries as night attire and are called *pajamas*.

"In the small-town jails I have met some honest and upstanding citizens who have been jailed as a substitute for some person who goes around scot-free. In these jails, a kind of childlike spirit rules over the prisoners. It is so powerful that as a means of innocent diversion they often urinate in their cell mate's shoes. Still, there is present among them a streak of generosity and no one dies of hunger, despite the so-called good intentions of the government which has cut, almost to the bone, the prisoners' mess, as something unnecessarily generous.

"The prisoner who has had food sent to him by his family shares it with another who has none. When a prisoner doesn't have a blanket, the rest of the prisoners cuss his mother up and down with all kinds of vulgarities, so that he will get boiling mad and thus keep himself warm. Oh, what exquisite banquets I have gotten for myself in some of these jails: a plate of rice or a stuffed pepper from my colleagues in exchange for an affectionate pat on the back or some expert legal advice from me, the shyster of all shysters.

"Life within our jails has a certain family atmosphere about it, and something of a religious brotherhood, complete with all the pacts and countersigns of a secret society.

"During the mornings, after the general delousing session, you sun yourself and at the same time plan your defense, made up your alibis, take care of business matters, and write letters intended for those on the outside. I have been the willing letter writer for hundreds of prisoners. My pen has been their eyes so that they could cry out their loneliness, and their mouths so that they could shout out their grievances, their means of remembering their unfortunate mothers and wives and children.

"After they give us something to eat—I find it inappropriate to use the word *lunch*—politics is the subject of conversation and the photographs of the political bigwigs from the hometowns are touched up—and no familiar detail is forgotten.

"In the afternoons, at that lonely moment when the sun sets, when the bars of the cells look like crosses bloodied by the criminal hand of twilight, these pitiful souls are strongly affected by memories of home and then, in a chorus, there surges forth their song, a song that is repeated again and again, with the sound of a sacred hymn, reverberating in the air like a painful wail of sorrow.

"The nights are just right for the obscene things, like memories of past sexual conquests and rather lewd and lusty stories. The prisoners are generous with their lies, one worse than the other, each thinking that the audience believes him as he describes unbelievable battles as an invincible knight on the imaginary battlefields of love. But, the others listen intently as they await their turn to dream out loud, and smile unbelievingly for they know that such things are told only as a means of achieving—all alone—that physical release which haunts them so. . . .

"One by one I recall the jails I have been in and I take great pride in having made some very fine friends in them.

"Once, I was sentenced to eight days in jail when, dressed in a new suit, wearing a bowler hat, and carrying a cane, I rang the bells of the parish church as a means of welcoming myself back home.

"Once when I was drunk in that populous city of Tancitaro, I shouted: 'Death to Hidalgo, the father of our Independence!' Fifteen days in jail! And I couldn't even convince the authorities that my shout in no way had influenced the death of such an illustrious hero who quite definitely had been shot a hundred years before I had made my proclamation.

83

"Once, in the city of Quiroga, when there was a poets festival, Grecian style, going on, I went out into the streets dressed only in a sheet, wearing a crown of flowers on my head—like an authentic Athenian. Eight days—cleaning the town square! And they gave me another eight days at hard labor for expressing the desire that a revolution break out so that Talion's law could be applied to the mayor of the town, making him sweep the entire town clean without any attire other than a headdress of feathers. This would have been the most appropriate dress for him inasmuch as he was indeed a savage.

"For setting myself up as a saviour of donkeys, one month in jail! Let me explain the situation to you so that I can answer the question which I see in your eyes.

"There was this mule driver, a friend of mine, who owned a little donkey which he had almost beaten to death. Very much moved by this little animal's bad luck, I made up my mind to free it from such insufferable slavery. With this end in mind, I asked its owner to rent the animal to me so that I could make a trip to Patzcuaro. As soon as we were out of town, I said to the humble little animal: 'The only way in which you can change your luck is to become the property of the first person who comes along.' The donkey agreed, letting out a loud hee-haw. And so I sold him to some mule drivers for twelve dollars without making out a bill of sale.

"When I got back to Santa Clara this inhuman man who had rented me the animal asked about his donkey and I answered: 'Please be informed that the unfortunate little animal died because of loneliness for you.' But this character started investigating and asking questions everywhere and finally they sentenced me to jail because they said that I had committed a robbery.

"Once I went to the town of Opopeo in order to preach the good word. I was dressed quite appropriately in my brother's cassock and had as my noble aim the desire to collect donations for our missions in Japan.

"Moved only by the desire to do good, I tried out my powers of persuasion for the benefit of those wayward sheep. And as payment for my generosity: one month in jail and ordered to make an immediate return of the donations I had collected, the latter being necessary in view of the fact that our Holy Mother the Church never loses and when she does, she takes what she can by force.

"My prayers to the Virgin Mary went unanswered. My sermons were fruitless! And take note of this irritating coincidence: I was explaining these words from the New Testament: 'I called to thee like the mother hen calls to her chicks, to protect you beneath my wing and ye did not come.' Boom! Those who came were the police and they hauled me down from the pulpit without the slightest display of respect for my religious garb. This is the way virtue is crushed underfoot in this world.

"On another occasion, Jesus, the baker, and I agreed to swap a rooster for a hen. I took my rooster to him, collected his hen, and because I ate the hen in a chicken potpie, five days in jail!"

"But Pito Perez, this punishment seems to be most unjust. I don't understand how there was any crime committed."

"That's the way I look at it, too, although I should explain how the whole affair took place:

"I heard Jesus say that he had a lot of hens and that he needed a rooster to satisfy this harem. I made a deal with him: One of my roosters in exchange for one of his hens. And he accepted my offer without asking what my feathered Don Juan was like. The only thing that he asked was if the animal still crowed. I said it did.

"At the stroke of midnight, I took my flute and walked to the street where Jesus lived. I stood near the gate to his house and began to play the best music of my repertoire: some popular dance pieces, a selection of some higher type music, and the *Qui Tollis* from Giuseppe Mercadante's *Mass*.

"Some would-be delinquents who were out on the town came down the street and stopped to listen to me play. One of them swore that the *Qui Tollis* that I was playing, that very holy and sacred music from the Mass, was *Amapola,* and that it had been written by the former President of Mexico, Lerdo de Tejada.

"I put the instrument in my pocket and then jumped the fence into the yard of Jesus' house. I reached out and grabbed the first sleeping hen I could find and jumped back over the fence into the street holding the chicken tightly in my arms.

"As I quickly hurried away from the spot, I left the following calling card for Jesus—a song:

> *To the friend with my name, 'So long!'*
> *In our deal I'm doing no wrong.*
> *For out of your pen,*
> *I've taken a hen,*
> *And left not a cock, but its song.*

Jesus swore that I had not legally fulfilled my end of the bargain and the judge sentenced me to pay him for the hen without taking into account at all the value of my music.

"On another occasion, while I was enjoying a meal under one of the arches that are there in downtown Jiquilpan, I said in a rather loud voice that there was such a scarcity of water in the town that they cooked their food in aguardiente and washed their hands in beer. Just for saying that, they took me away and locked me up. But it turned out that when I explained my crime to the judge, one Enrique

Farias, a very honorable person, he let out a loud roar of laughter and exclaimed: 'That's terrific, my friend!' and he ordered my immediate release.

"I remember a rather tragic episode which took place in the jail in Yuriria, one of those incidents that writers use when they write those novels that are now called psychoanalytic novels and which used to be called pulp novels.

"I had been spending my time meandering through the towns and the ranches of that region, asking those Christian souls for donations in order to construct a temple on the top of Mt. Lebanon. When I reached the town of Yuriria, in the state of Guanajuato, I was stopped by the police because the mayor of the town had received a letter which read as follows:

ARREST JESUS PEREZ GAONA, A FRAUDULENT MISSIONARY WHO IS PASSING HIMSELF OFF AS A CARMELITE MONK. PERSONAL DESCRIPTION: HE GOES BY THE NAME OF PITO PEREZ.

R. ITURBIDE
MAYOR OF MORELIA

"In the jail in Yuriria, I met a prisoner who was very much feared by the others because of his violent and vengeful character. His name was Rosendo and, in addition to the other bloody crimes he had committed, he was now serving a sentence for murder. He had killed a man who had dared to charge him some twenty cents for pasturing a cow. But what really astonished the people was the behavior of the dead man's widow after the murder of her husband. She was a quiet, pleasant woman whom I used to see bring food every day to Rosendo's cell.

"The other prisoners filled me in on her story:

"A short time after the crime, this woman went to the jail in search of her husband's murderer, almost as if she were thankful for what he had done. For two years she worked diligently to support the prisoner who, in the beginning, seemed to distrust this rather strange behavior. But her perseverance and her tenderness succeeded in wiping out any fears the prisoner had. Vain, like all men, he accepted everything, explaining it to himself in the following way:

" 'This unfortunate woman must have suffered a great deal while living with the deceased. May he rest in peace! And she wants to thank me because I ended all her miseries with one bullet.'

"While I was still a prisoner in that jail, Rosendo succeeded in getting out on bail. The widow who had befriended him came to meet him when he was set free. We all ran to the barred window of the jail to see Apolinaria, for that was her name, dressed in her red percale dress and her new shoes, and her blue shawl, sprinkled with white dots, tossed casually around her shoulders. She waited faithfully for him, just as if he were her husband. When he came out, she carried his few possessions and they walked toward her house as if nothing in the world had happened.

"She offered him a tasty lunch and afterwards, her simple but inviting bed. Calmly and without any anxieties, she let him lead her over to it. A sweet light came from her eyes and there was a sad smile on her lips. They closed the doors and the room was enveloped in that darkness in which only a blindfolded Cupid can see.

"Suddenly, a horrible scream was heard from the house! The neighbors nearby were terrified.

" 'What's happened? Where did that shout come from?'

"At the very instant in which Rosendo had reached his climax and his entire body was trembling and shuddering from the orgasm, the woman cautiously had opened a straight-edged razor. With one stroke she sliced off the victorious organs of this would-be lover, whom the police later found naked and dead. Apolinaria looked at him with that sweet light that continued to come from her eyes. 'I have kept the promise I made to my dead husband,' she exclaimed calmly. 'Take me away.'

"I have served time in many jails and for many reasons: for being drunk, for being a musician, for being a missionary, and once, for being a fool. The last mentioned reason is the only one that has ever bothered my conscience.

"I had arrived in Ario de Rosales looking for work. I offered my services as a druggist, as a barber, as a sacristan in the church, and I also made the rounds to the various courts in session to see if anyone wanted to have any papers served. All to no avail! Either my appearance, at first sight, did not inspire confidence, or the people of the town had adopted that most American of all doctrines: 'Ario for the Arians.'

"Later I went down to the poolhall which was owned by one Mr. Medal, who also owned a drugstore in town. I waited around the place, hoping that some pigeon would show, some sucker from whom I could filch a buck or two. Now I am a pretty good pool-shark, one of those who can get all of the balls on one side of the table and then make shots worth thirty points each, all the while assuring my opponent this is the first time I have ever held a cue stick in my hands.

" 'Hey,' the owner shouted to me. 'Are you the fellow who came by this morning looking for work? Well, if you know how to write and you have a sample of your work, I can give you a job.'

" 'I have penned my way through every kind of letter there is and I have read the *Spanish and American Sampler*. I think you can tell from this if I'm worth anything.'

" 'Have you had any journalistic experience?'

" 'I once had a free subscription to the magazine *Lotus Flower*, published in Morelia.'

" 'Well, I will give you two dollars a day for being the Executive Administrator of a bi-weekly publication which I get out every three months. In fact, tomorrow I am publishing the second edition. So, what do you think of this job?'

" 'I accept,' I answered.

"On the following day I went back to the drug-store to get instructions from my new boss. He made me sign a receipt for two dollars, which he said he was going to give me later, and told me to circulate around town so that I could become thoroughly acquainted, as he termed it, with the needs of the people. After walking up and down the streets, I went to the town square and sat down on one of the benches there. A few minutes later, the Chief of Police arrived and he told me that the Prefect wanted to see me.

"We went to his honor's office and he questioned me, heatedly, waving in my face a newspaper which he had in his hand. 'Are you responsible for this article about me?'

" 'And the *Admin.*, too,' I answered, abbreviating the word *administrator* for him.

" 'You brazen, stupid fool! Are you trying to make me the laughingstock of town? Well, my friend, it's off to jail with you, but not before you eat this paper right in front of me!'

"He forced me to eat the newspaper, and he made me chew it slowly—like it was tasty—just as if I were eating some delicious tidbit.

"I found out later that the druggist had used my position as Administrator of the newspaper for his own ends and in that edition he had ridiculed and criticized the mayor up and down, calling him, among other nice things, a thief and a murderer. All of that for the two dollars a day which he had promised me—money which I never saw—all of which indeed was a just punishment for my own stupidity.

"I spent the forty days of Lent cooped up in that jail. Well, not exactly all forty days since they let me out on Palm Sunday. But, because the other prisoners and I had prepared a Holy Week ceremony with real people instead of painted images and I was to play the part of our Lord, Jesus Christ, I was very anxious to drain the chalice of all of its bitterness, even down to the last dregs. And so I stayed in jail just so I could be crucified.

"In the scene of The Last Supper, the twelve prisoners who were present really seemed to be true apostles. They had long, flowing beards, wore red robes, and their eyes were devoid of all hope.

"I washed their feet amid an outburst of sneezes

and then we left the large wardroom and went into the patio, which was completely flooded with moonlight, in order that they might capture me on the Mount of Olives.

"An alcoholic stupor had come over my entourage and so they really couldn't see Judas at that moment when he gave me the kiss of betrayal. It was a pretended kiss, to be acted out, nothing more. But the prisoner who was playing the role of Judas staunchly refused to give it to me, swearing that he was not a queer.

" 'Arise,' I ordered in a very loud voice. St. Peter got up first and whipping out his sword, he sliced the air, aiming at the servant of the High Priest. The prisoner who was playing the part of the servant jumped back quickly and exclaimed: 'For Christ's sake, what the hell's wrong with you?'

"In the next scene they took me from pillar to post, that is from Herod to Pilate who, after judging me and sentencing me to be crucified, couldn't wash his hands. In the first place, there was no wash basin and in the second place he had no hands.

"The cock crowed three times and Peter, who did not want to deny me, shouted out most furiously: 'I know my buddy here and I do not deny it! We Mexicans are men among men!'

"The hour for my crucifixion arrived. They stripped me of my robe which, this time, really did disappear and then they tied me very tightly to a cross. They didn't crucify the two thieves, Dismas and Gestas, because there weren't any more crosses available. But they told them to stand on either side of me with their arms stretched out to look like crosses and to guard me. The role of Dismas was played by an ex-postmaster who had a great many children and had been sentenced for embezzlement. And the role of Gestas was played by a rather heroic wino whose only medals were those which had popped out on his face in the form of multicolored pimples.

"And the seven last pronouncements of Christ came serenely from my lips:

" 'Father, punish them; they pretend that they know not what they do!'

" 'Verily, I say unto thee, today shalt thou be with me in Paradise—if thou can escape from this crummy jail.'

" 'Woman, behold thy sons! Sons, why do thee lie so much to thy innocent mothers?'

" 'My God, my God, why hast Thou forsaken us in this sad dungeon?'

" 'I thirst.'

(" 'I'll buy a beer for the Lord,' said St. Peter unbuttoning the small leather purse tied to his belt.)

" 'Times have changed: Man does not live by the words of God alone . . .'

"Looking at the empty bottles which were strewn all around the floor, I exclaimed in a tone of distress:

" 'Well boys, the party's over! . . .'

"The ropes which bound my arms were hurting me and it was impossible for me to support myself in that position any longer. I began to shout in a loud voice:

" 'Untie me! I'm tired! Take me down! I can't go on!'

"But the other prisoners only laughed at my turmoil. And they turned their backs on me with that same indifference with which humanity turned its back on Christ and watched Him die, dangling from a wooden cross . . ."

Pito Perez never returned to the belltower. And he left his story only half finished, perhaps because he had found too much pleasure in looking down the mouths of bottles hoping to discover another world, a world more humane, more generous. Would he be successful in finding that new world in the crystal clarity of wine? Maybe! But, this is why we saw him wandering aimlessly from tavern to tavern, his shoes torn to shreds and his mop of dirty hair topped with a crown of flowers.

Part Two

"... because there is no
pain to compare with the
pain of dying ..."

Pito Perez

In May, it is very hot in Morelia. The people grow thin from the heat and the children complain of stomachaches.

"It's because of the first of the new fruit," say the mothers who chat back and forth in their living rooms. "But when the first rains come, the city will come back to its senses."

Even the sun feels that it is asphyxiated and tries to escape, tearing through the white walls of the city with its blond rays, much like the clown who jumps through a paper hoop while his trained horse gallops at full speed.

During these hot spells, there are few people on

the streets, and so their footsteps resound on the sidewalks like a well-wound clock striking the hours of the day.

It is eight o'clock in the morning. Mrs. Pachita Perez Gil hurries down the street on her way to the Church of the Cross. Several generations of college students have called her *Grandma* although she looks more like a contented abbot hurrying along behind a belly filled with virtues.

At nine o'clock, Adolfo Cano walks to his law office. In his eyes there is a devilish gleam, but it is not concerned with the clauses of a contract nor the legal wording of some document. Rather, he is thinking about how his three kings won the pot over three queens.

They tell how once as he was eating dinner, with his head leaning well over his plate and his mind a thousand miles away, his wife asked:

"Do you want another slice of bread, Adolfo?"

"I call and raise you ten more," answered the lawyer from the faraway land of the Ace of Spades. And taking the stack of bread, he began to deal the slices to his children, just as if it were a deck of cards.

At eleven o'clock is heard the single, long stride of the one-legged man who sells cheese:

"Cottage cheese! sour cream! cheese!" And with the end of his wooden leg, he rapidly taps the stone blocks as a signal to his customers that he is here.

At three in the afternoon, the steps of Lorenzo

Olaciregui, Dean of the Cathedral, are heard as he makes his way to the choir loft.

A clicking of heels, in two-four time, *presto, vivace,* resounds on the stone sidewalk as Maestro Mier hurries to give his piano lessons.

Professor Gallegos isn't heard as he walks along because he walks softly on the edges of his twenty bunions and he hardly touches the ground. He stops at each corner and talks aloud to himself, with that same eloquence which has caused him so much trouble simply because what he says is absolutely incomprehensible. Everybody remembers, for example, the time when his house caught fire. Professor Gallegos, dressed in his underwear, ran from his house, shouting for help:

"Nocturnal guard! Hasten thy steps on the wings of Mercury. Cause to vibrate that mournful concave artifice of bronze ere the most voracious of nature's elements consumes this, my humble abode."

The policeman looked at him, stupefied, without moving from the spot. And the professor's house went up in flames.

And the shame of being insulted by a charcoal dealer?

"Bucolic dweller of the somber woods, what value do you place on this bundle of calcined fagots which you place upon the damaged scapulae of this rustic ass?"

"Rustic ass? That'll be you, dingbat. The rich

are proud they're rich just so's they can humiliate the poor. . . ."

Up Thieves Alley there comes the slow, rhythmic tinkle of bells. It isn't the Holy Sacrament going to pay a visit on a dying man, nor is it a lead mare leading a few horses up from the hot lands.

The people know full well what the bells are announcing and they run to the doors of their homes to wait for this odd and eccentric peddler.

A thin man walks slowly down the street. His face has been tanned by the sun and his hair is so long it touches lightly on his shoulder. On each arm he carries a huge basket. And little bells dangle from each handle of the baskets, from the brim of his hat, from the tail of his coat. Bells of all sizes swing back and forth, from one that is the size of a cowbell to those very minute bells that adorn a shepherd's crook and tinkle so sprightly during the Christmas season. Their sounds are happy sounds, like the chatter of little children as they play at their games.

Hidden in those baskets, as in the hands of a master of the sleight of hand, is a full stock of items: shoelaces, barbers' combs, fine-tooth combs, fasteners, embroidered hems for ladies' dresses, silk hose, face powder, waxy cord and thread.

"Hey peddler! Got any hair curlers?" asks a young lady from behind a half-open door.

"For every part of your body, ma'am."

"How much are your silk stockings?"

"Two-fifty for real silk."

"Can't you come down a little on your price?"

"You can have them free, my sweet, if I can put them on you."

The bells respectfully become silent when they hear their master's voice. When the deal is finished, they start to sing again and slowly they move up the street, tinkling merrily and announcing the wares they have for sale.

The man with the bells is Pito Perez. Seeing me standing there on the corner, he puts his portable general store on the ground so that he can talk to me more easily.

"It sure has been a long time since we have seen each other! Not since the bell tower in Santa Clara. Why, that's almost ten years. . ."

"That's true, Pito Perez. And you left unfinished the story of your life."

"To go on living it, my friend, and to have something to talk about. That whirlwind, the Revolution, came down from the north and those of us without roots were sent flying. It raised the dry dust; it scattered the rotted leaves. It made the timid birds flee and even chased away the parasites who take over the crops. But, speaking in plain language, without the use of metaphors, I'm talking about the rich, the clergy, the lazy people, the adventurers.

"The trees which produce year after year remained unmoved, as did the bare rocks of the hills; the men who work their fields: oak trees deeply rooted in the earth, the Indians: solid rocks from time immemorial which can only be uprooted by a cyclone, a cyclone which would destroy them, but at the same time one which would smash to bits that soft, rose-colored stone that corrupt cities are made of."

"Bravo, Pito Perez! I left you a cynical philosopher and now I find you converted into a political orator."

"And you could say that being a political orator demands more cynicism than being the cynical philosopher. Yes, that's right. But, the two can't be confused: the politician has his heart in his stomach and the philosopher has his heart in his head."

"How about a drink, Pito? Or a bottle?"

"Well, that depends on which key you want to use to open the safe of my confidential material. Remember the deal we made some time ago!"

"But I find you changed. You no longer wear the Prince Albert coat, which was your classic garb. You have given up your cane and your hat for these baskets filled with junk and those bells which don't seem to have any real purpose at all."

"Well, I have the bells for two reasons: so I won't wear out my voice hawking my wares and to keep alive the memory of my travels throughout my beloved Michoacan. Do I make myself clear? Look, every one of the bells bears an inscription: the name of one of the towns in Michoacan, or the name of the bells in those towns. And as I walk through the streets, sweating under the weight of my baskets, I listen to them as they talk among themselves, as they tell of what they have seen or of the lives they have lived. . .

"The big bell from Patzcuaro, scolds its little sister from Quiroga because when she rings she sticks her tongue out at the lake.

"The bells from Zamora beat their breasts with their clappers, like young novitiates who have been persistently plagued by evil thoughts.

"The bell from Tacambaro screams itself hoarse, shouting: 'Long live the Revolution!' The bell from Tzintzunzan gets its tongue all twisted as it prays in the Tarascan Indian language to a god which isn't its own. And the old bell from Zitacuaro still sheds its big, bronze tears over the disaster of '65.

"The bell from Tinguindin tinkles merrily. The one from Tirindaro sings. The one from Paracho causes some pretty wild dancing. The one from Irimbo, like a symbol of peace, signals the rest period for the overworked laborers.

"These here, next to my heart, are bells from my own part of the state. This one, from Guanoncha, signals the first light of holy days; this one, from the convent, tolls for the dead; this tiny, silver bell represents the parish bell which my hands, numb from the morning cold, so often rang to call the people to the first mass of the day.

"Bells of Michoacan, ring out, all together, for Pito Perez passes by; Pito Perez, glorious in his misery and proud in his rags!"

"You are indeed a human carillon."

"That I am. Sometimes I ring hallelujah, sometimes psalms of penance. But each one of my bells brings vividly to mind the memory of some village, just as my eyes saw it. And their voices are imitations of the voices of my friends who tell me what they have done by the way they act. Listening to my bells, I usually forget my customers and pass them by in order not to interrupt the tinkling chatter.

"Then, my customers say, in a somewhat burlesque tone:

" 'Pito Perez is drunk again.'

"Drunk? Yes, I am, but drunk on memories: laughter, tears, profanity, song—just as in those long-gone days of my youth."

"And Pito Perez, the musician?"

"I don't know what happened to him! I lost my flute in some jail, or some other of a thousand places where I have slept off my drunks, But, with the same honesty that has always characterized my shamelessness, I must warn you that I am no longer a respectable drunk. Not even an ingenious one. Children make fun of me; shopkeepers rob me; the police humiliate me. And when I'm stretched out somewhere on some bench, with my workshop open and my master craftsman asleep, no kind soul even attempts to cover my nakedness with a newspaper. Respectable people are disgusted by me and avoid me. They are repulsed by my repugnant appearance, by the stench of sour wine, by my filthy hands which no one, not even my friends, will shake, always pretending that they are reaching for a handkerchief. And do you know what they call me now? Waxy Cord! Waxy Cord, the nickname for a common peddler, for some uncouth person—not a name for an artist like me. I'm telling you all this just in case you might be ashamed of me and not want to talk to me."

"Don't think such things, Pito Perez. Come back here tonight, to the Central Bar, so we can talk like we did in the old days."

Pito Perez promised to do as I had asked and, lifting his junk-laden baskets, he walked away, his ears tuned to his own music, that music which, according to the ups-and-downs of the street, was happy or sad, boisterous or listless.

"Good evening to one and all," said Pito Perez as he walked into the tavern.

His appearance was the same as I had known it ten years before: a ragged and worn Prince Albert coat with a flower in his buttonhole, a cane with a nickle-plated handle, a pair of trousers so baggy at the knees that he could have kept his children in them, just like a kangaroo. He wore his wide-brimmed straw hat which was balanced precariously on his uncombed mop of hair and which, because of its color like old gold, looked like the halo of a saint.

"And your baskets, Pito Perez?"

"I'm not here as a businessman now. At this hour

of the night, the needles and the barbers' combs are home sleeping with childlike innocence. I come to these gatherings like those mothers who, after having put their children to sleep, get together at dusk to talk about their offspring's clever antics of the day."

"What have you been doing in all these years since we have seen each other, Pito Perez?"

"Drinking, to get drunk, and then drinking to cure my hangovers; drinking, that is, until *delirium tremens* takes over completely and I fall over in the gutter of some street, completely unconscious and half-dead.

"Death and I have been on very friendly terms for quite some time now. She toys with me without hurting me. The dangers from which I have escaped, probably because of her help! Once, when I was completely plastered, which is now the perfect state for me, I fell into a river and without knowing how or when, I was saved. Like a great general, I have marched victorious over battlefields strewn with dead, breathing in the stench of rotted flesh, and I have seen how the eyes of the dead take on a celluloid-like shine when the light of life leaves their body. In a state of ecstasy, brought on by alcoholic compassion, I have rubbed the cold feet of a dead man, in an attempt to warm them. While in a hospital, I once welcomed two of my drinking friends who, with that complacent smile of a person who gives someone a box of candy, brought me four large death-candles. And I listened to one of them as he stuttered and stammered, expressing his condolences at my passing and asking to be excused from accompanying me to the cemetery the next day because he had some deal to put over.

"With true sorrow and grief, I have wept over my sad remains and I have felt that there is no pain to compare with the pain of dying. Nevertheless here I am, watching over my very own mourning with some of the sap of life still left in me."

"But where was it that you were exposed to so many dangers?"

"Figure it out for yourself! I have been the guest of a goodly number of hospitals where, if the patients don't die of the illness that brought them there in the first place, they succumb to hunger or die the victim of some clinical experiment.

"I was in the hospital of St. Vincent de Paul, and just to keep alive, we patients had to go out into the street and beg from door to door. There were patients who were so sick with typhus that they scarcely had strength to keep their blankets wrapped around them and who died on the thresholds of the very houses where they had gone to beg.

"In the hospital of the Holy Refuge we patients used to dance in the garden, starting in the early hours of the morning, and the only clothing that we had were some sheets of doubtful cleanliness. We used to cut dandelions, little bunches of rosemary, and other weeds and plants which we boiled in a single, common pot and which constituted the only food which that vegetarian society had. What a fantastic sight it was to see us, those enormous white butterflies, flying from dandelion to dandelion— flying is the word, because there wasn't a single ounce of flesh on our bodies!

"Being the most optimistic of the lot, I used to advise them, saying: 'Friends, let's try the hollyhocks for dessert.'

"I struggled endlessly to convince my frail dining companions that those weeds tasted like breast of chicken.

"'My friends, overcome reality,' I used to preach to them. 'Dine with your imagination, like those starving persons who give themselves spiritual banquets by looking into the windows of bakery shops. Follow my example: I eat boiled violets as a sign of good breeding; the aristocrats like them coated with sugar as a means of being inspired, as a way of awakening their poetic talents.'

"I was in the hospital in Cotija. Of the twenty-eight patients who were there, I am the only one who is still living. Let me tell you what happened:

"The director was a distinguished botanist, a man who had been quoted frequently in the medical textbooks. This wise and eminent man had classified scientifically more than 20,000 plants from among the flora of our country and he tested their therapeutic properties on us, specifying dosage at the cost of the patient. And what if a patient died, dehydrated by the diarrhea which had been caused by the liquid from some bitter gourd? Well, reduce the dosage on the next person and forget about that poor victim who had been sacrificed on the altar of science.

"I was successful in escaping the scientific shenanigans of this famous physician by jumping the wall of the hospital, just at the right time, and fleeing. He ran after me, promising that he would put to work the totality of his five senses to cure me. But I, from a distance, shouted back to him: 'So far as poisons are concerned, make mine tequila.'"

"Well, that may be the case, Pito, but where did all these illnesses come from?"

"From that world-famous poison, alcohol. According to historians, in the old days kings used to partake of the most potent poisons to get their bodies used to them, to immunize themselves so to speak, in the event of any attempt on their lives. This doesn't work for us drunkards because the more we drink, the more we become attached to the effects our drinking causes. But, let me go on with the itinerary of my misadventures.

"Only by a miracle performed by Death, who, as I have already said, is my best friend, was I able to escape from the hospital in Morelia. There was a very kind and warmhearted nurse who worked there.

Her name was Pelagia and this name was a very bad omen for the suspicious people who were to be treated by her. Pelagia was born in the Hoyo del Aire region, in the city of Taretan. She completed her medical studies in a single day and received her nurses' license at that very moment when she was hired to work as a maid in the hospital. They stuck a white cap on her head, tied on her a long apron which dragged along the floor, and put her to work in the middle of a ward for mental patients without even inquiring if there was a head beneath that hat and if there was, were there any brains in that head or if it was some little gourd filled with pebbles from the creek.

"When the medical visitations were made, Pelagia followed the doctor from bed to bed, picking up the prescriptions which the physician had written, filling them later in the hospital's pharmacy. Pelagia talked endlessly of those patients under her care:

" 'Number 13 didn't sleep too good last night and jist in case he was hungry, I brung him a sardine sandwich; knocked him out for a while! Number 4 took six stinking craps which I have kept for you jist in case you was wantin' to examine them, scientific like. Number 9 ain't so sick no more, I think. Last night *he* wanted to give *my* fanny a rub-down."

"When Pelagia returned from the pharmacy with the prescriptions filled, she would stop in the doorway of the ward and shout to us in a most jubilant tone, much like a mother who has just returned from taking a walk and who has brought some candy for her children:

" 'Here is your medicine. Let's see. Who wants pills? Who wants liquid? Who wants powders?'

"And then she would give each of the patients what he asked for, despite the danger of killing all of us. She hadn't taken too well to me, as I said before, and so she always gave me the enemas which had been prescribed for other patients.

" 'The enemas are for this wise guy,' she used to say, 'because he can get drunk on anything, even capsules.'

"Perhaps that is why I didn't kick the bucket because no dangerous poisons are ever prescribed for that other mouth.

"Political ideas were another danger in that hospital. There were some physicians who were religious fanatics and they paid great attention to those patients who always took communion. And, there were some freethinking physicians who didn't take too kindly to those patients who didn't think the same way. When I talked to those who belonged to the first group, I used to tell them about my brother, the priest, and when I talked to those of the second group I used to tell them that I belonged to a branch of the Hussites and that when I drank wine on fast days it was in order to receive one of our sacraments.

One Doctor Ortiz agreed with my doctrines and permitted me to take communion every morning with a glass of fine muscatel wine which the dispensary gave to me on his orders.

"Some days I took communion as many as three times, because I knew it was a practice favorable for the salvation of my soul.

"Of course, this routine marked the beginning of my getting well and the return of my inner self to its normal state. My long periods of drunkenness always ended up with an attack of *delirium tremens* and these attacks always transported me to regions undreamed of by the rest of mankind. In my delirium, I reach a peak of exalted hyper-ecstasy, one filled with hallucinations.

"One time I thought I was a tree. My feet were the roots and my legs the trunk and ants of all sizes were crawling up and down my harsh and rough bark. This army of tiny creatures tickled my wrinkled skin with their wiry feet and thus set my nerves on edge. I watched them climb up and up, and a sudden desire came over me: brush them off, knock them far away from me. But I hesitated as an idea came to my mind: trees have an obligation to help these parasites, children of Nature just as are the trees, and therefore all brothers. 'If I am a tree,' I concluded, 'I must permit them to creep and to climb up and down my trunk, to eat my flesh.' And so that my hands would not interfere with those defensless creatures, I stretched out my arms, toward the heavens, and the sky rewarded me by converting my arms into branches, green, fresh, flowery branches.

"I no longer felt the tickling sensation caused by the insects. Rather, I felt the flow of sweet sap in my veins, a sap which gave life to little buds whose velvet-like leaves swayed gently in the breeze and sang an *allegro* of Spring.

"Birds of many colors came to take refuge in my branches. They were the thoughts of my entire life, which had returned to their nests: hummingbirds drunk on the nectar of flowers, mockingbirds which sang the melodies of my old flute; swallows of love, shy and fleeting; parrots which shrieked their senseless babbling and their vulgar words; and the shy and philosophical owl, symbol of my melancholy.

"I was a new tree in the forest. But I was soon cut down by the blows of reality. My delirium ended and I returned once again to the sterile form of mortal man."

"Pito Perez, you old drunkard, you. You're crazy!"

"And why not a poet?

"On another occasion, I was stretched out on a hard, rickety old bed. Slowly but surely I felt myself being transformed into a large piece of cloth, one of those silken cloths which rustles with a sensual swishiness at the slightest touch.

"With my own eyes I saw myself droop over the sides of the bed, like a large curtain that hangs above a flag-bedecked balcony. My hands and my feet were dangling tufts of gold and on my stomach there were wrinkles and rumples, as if someone had leaned his elbows on my body, watching the army of centuries go by. Later I felt myself being cut with some enormous scissors and my pieces being sewn together to make a suit for a little boy, a little boy whose parents wouldn't let him move for fear that he would tear his new clothes. I was concerned, too, fearful that the boy would drag me across the floor or slide me along the handrail of the stairway. My flesh suffered the pain of seeing itself bruised and torn and no one heard my silent cry of despair.

"I breathed a sigh of relief when I saw that the cloth of my body had taken on a rose-colored tinge and an unusual luster. Then I issued a command to my imagination:

" 'I want to be a chemise, to belong to a beautiful woman, to feel the touch of her warm and perfumed body. I am going to sin, at least once, without being scorned or hated, without being driven away because of my repugnance. In a festival of light and with every thread of my body, I shall cast my eyes into the most hidden corners of another body. With every fiber in my body, I shall have this woman of my desires. My pleasure will rise in voluptuous waves, from the needlework on the hem up to the little bows around the neck. And once my pleasure has been quenched, I will sleep, snug against an alabaster body, and dream the dream of dreams.'

"And the miracle became reality! My folds descended over delicate hips; I was drooped over snow-white shoulders; I was moulded over breasts whose nipples offended my sensitivities—like a needle offends the cloth it pierces. But, I began to feel the uncomfortable coolness of fresh air; I sneezed through every fiber, just as if I had taken cold. And it was because that feminine figure, in all its pagan nudity, was an inert marble statue and her cold touch had awakened me from my delirium."

"And now that you are telling these things, Pito Perez, wouldn't we be correct in thinking that you have gotten a little out of touch with reality?"

"But, can you tell me which is my reality and which is my dream? I am certain that everything that I see exists and that Death has loaned me her eyes so that I can see with supernatural powers and thus amuse myself with the landscapes of other worlds.

"One night I thought I had a dagger on my person and I wanted to get rid of it because I am a man of peace and I hate all kinds of weapons, even while on my greatest drunken binges. I drew it out of the sheath and threw it high up into the air saying:

" 'I don't want to see you anymore. Hide, hide yourself in space.'

"The dagger went high into the sky, and as it came down, it ripped open the curtains of the heavens with its sharp point. And then, those curtains opened like the flaps of a soldier's tent.

"Curiously my eyes peered through the tear into that unknown world. And I suddenly realized that I was looking into Paradise!

"The trees were colored an artificial green and they looked like Christmas trees, loaded down with toys and candies. The meadow was a tapestry from the period of Louis XV with large roses embroidered in it. In the center of the sky the sun shot out its rays, like an iridescent chandelier with almond-shaped crystals. And on the translucent walls saints were hanging, real saints who looked like paintings in oil. These revered gentlemen chatted with each other from their frames, or they discussed Catholic dogma, interrupted by Saint Augustine who emphatically repeated as an answer to everything: 'I have spoken.' All the while his teacher, Saint Ambrose, was composing and humming in a low voice a liturgical theme which Saint Gregory the Great was expanding by means of his divine counterpoint.

"Underneath a big, round tree, Job and St. Simeon Stylites, surrounded by some lesser saints, were playing a game of chess. St. Simeon scratched his head in despair and said to those who surrounded him:

" 'Job has spent twenty-five years at this chess board, and he still hasn't figured out this play!'

121

"Dressed in a linen tunic and wearing a snow-white beard, which was his flag of peace, a venerable old man majestically watched over the flock of white sheep. Looking at them carefully, I noted that the sheep had human faces and each was wearing a little tag around his neck. On each tag was written the person's name and the date on which he had entered Paradise. Each sheep had some insignia of its profession on Earth: faithful husbands who had been deceived had twisted horns; women who had committed adultery wore an innocent smile; the female followers of Bacchus who had repented indicated their price in coin, in clothes, and in gifts; the beatified fools wore their ribbons and other regal trappings of vanity.

"Some fat, wooly sheep were wandering around, showing off their tags which indicated that they had willed their earthly goods to the Church; others with languid eyes and with tufts of wool curled into little ringlets were the Magdalens of questionable sex who had been pardoned for having loved too much. Some sheep wore the epaulets of a general, a rank they had gained for having fought and killed—in a most Christian manner—the enemies of their religion.

"I saw some skinny lambs with their private parts painted gold and on their foreheads they wore the crowns of martyrs. The placards which they wore round their necks read: 'I married a rich woman and I soon discovered what it means to fornicate by necessity.'

"Some little sheep with sad eyes scampered about and rubbed themselves against the tree trunks. They were the most virtuous of virgins who had defended their maidenhood at all costs.

"Some fat, long-haired ewes were stretched out on the grass. Everytime they heard some steps, they got up and looked down the road. They were the wives of the gamblers and the drunkards who had spent their lives constantly waiting for their night-owl mates to come home.

"I stuck my head through the curtains and I saw a fat priest with a tray in his hands. He was practicing at collecting alms in order not to lose the knack.

" 'Father,' I asked him, 'aren't there any black sheep here?'

" 'No, my simple brother. The black sheep are the poor on Earth. But since there are so many and because they do not fit in here, we take care of them in Purgatory, or in Limbo.'

" 'And if they do not merit such treatment?'

" 'The poor deserve any treatment they get. Besides, what would they gain by rebelling? Hell, like Lucifer.'

"Frightened by such celestial justice, so similar to ours here on Earth, I quickly hurried away from this blue curtain and cursed the dagger which had unfolded this mystery before my eyes."

"You poor, unfortunate Pito Perez Your mind gets tangled up and then untangled, just like a ball of waxy cord!"

Smiling maliciously, someone in the group asked Pito Perez:

"And Caneca?"

"She's at home, surrounded by all the comforts of life."

"Who is Caneca?" I asked, curious to find out about this person.

"The most faithful love I have had in all my life!"

"But, Pito Perez, are you living with a woman?"

"For quite some time now, ever since the day I stole her away from the hospital in Zamora.

"They had her locked up in a room next to the administration office. I only saw her once, but that was enough to make me decide to take her with me. And so I did.

"The night before my departure I was able to get her out of her hiding place and to sleep with her, both of us in the same bed. This was done, of course, with the help and aid of the other patients. When dawn came, I left the hospital with her without the watchman's finding out.

"We took the road to Uruapan and crossed the mountains at Purepero Pass. We slept high in the hills because I thought it dangerous to go into any of the towns with her because the suspicious nature of the people could have caused me some difficulties. How cautious I had to be on this journey and how long this trip seemed to take!

"One evening, at dusk, a farmer saw me walking through a pasture. He almost fainted!

"In Uruapan, I went to a friend's house to put up for the night, but his wife raised the roof when she found out that I would be in their house accompanied by this woman. With tears and with rantings, she asked her husband to throw us out. She said that it was a great sin for them to permit us to stay under their roof and my friend could not convince her that the whole thing was really unimportant. Oh, the superstitions of ignorant people!

"We finally got to Morelia, by train, but in order to protect her from indiscreet glances, I had to hide her in a basket in which she suffered a great deal and she soon hurt in all her joints. Oh, the poor thing! But with my anatomical knowledge, and with loving care, I was soon able to restore her to her regular self.

"Now I am living with her, much to my contentment. She patiently waits for me to come home, always having a drink ready for me. She sleeps next to me, or rather, I should say, she watches over my sleep, never closing those eyes in whose depths there is only tenderness.

> Caneca, my sweet.
> She roams not the street.
> And never does she want something to eat!"

"That's fine, Pito Perez. But, who is this person? Such mystery about traveling with a woman—and her great virtue—all of this seems incomprehensible to me."

"Well, who else can it be! It is the skeleton of a woman, carefully assembled by a physician in Zamora and used by the students and interns in the hospital in their study of anatomy."

"How horrible! Aren't you afraid to go to bed with a skeleton?"

"Afraid? Why should I be? Aren't we even more repugnant skeletons, covered as we are with rotted flesh? And still knowing all of this, we look for contact with women. My woman has no body functions to worry about. She does not have body odor. Neither does she demand anything in the way of clothes or jewelry. She is not a coquette, or a chatterbox, or a religious fanatic, nor is she capricious. Quite the contrary, she is the model of all virtue. How lucky I was to meet up with her!

"Here is her picture. Meet Mrs. Pito Perez, that's her holding her husband's arm. Look at her big eyes, her white teeth, and notice that over her heart she wears a sprig of orange blossoms like the one I wear pinned to the lapel of my jacket.

"The Epistle of St. Paul says that marriage ends only in death. Mine began with death and will last throughout all eternity."

"You are stark raving mad, Pito Perez!"

"Don't you believe it," replied the owner of the Central Bar. "Ask him to sell you something out of his baskets on credit and you will see that he may be crazy, but he's not stupid."

"Too much talk and too little wine," answered Pito Perez.

"Drinks to everyone," I ordered, "although it seems to me somewhat paradoxical to drink a toast to the health of a dead woman. But, let's drink one anyway: to Pito Perez and to his respectable consort."

The early risers in the neighborhood found the body on a pile of rubbish. Its hair was completely disheveled and caked with mud. Its mouth had contracted into a convulsive grin of bitterness Its wide-open eyes looked at the heavens with a challenging haughtiness.

The only clothes that covered the body were a dirty jacket and a threadbare pair of pants, tied at the waist with a piece of rope. They called the police and one of the persons, carefully examining the face of the dead man, said:

"This man is Waxy Cord, the peddler with the bells."

They brought a stretcher and laid the body on it. Out of the pocket of his jacket some papers and a picture fell. It was a picture of the dead man smiling, arm in arm with Death.

On one of the papers, written in pencil, there was the following:

LAST WILL AND TESTAMENT

"To Humanity, I bequeath the entire lot of my bitterness.

"To the rich, hungry for gold, I leave the excrement of my life.

"To the poor, because they are so cowardly, I will my contempt—because they do not rise and seize everything in one final stroke of supreme justice. Miserable slaves of a church which preaches resignation to them; miserable slaves of a government which asks complete submission without giving them anything in return!

"I believed in no one! I respected no one! Why? Because no one believed in me, because no one respected me. Only fools or lovers give of themselves without some conditions.

"LIBERTY, EQUALITY, FRATERNITY!

"What a ridiculous farce. Liberty is murdered by those who have power. Equality is destroyed by money. And Fraternity dies at the hands of our own miserable egoism.

"You miserable slaves, if you still have one breath

of hope, do not stop to listen to the voice of the Apostles. Your ideal is to rise—and to remain on high, despite all obstacles.

"If Jesus did not attempt to renounce his being God, what can you expect of man?

"Humanity, I know you! I have been one of your victims!

"As a child you took from me all learning and gave it to my brothers so that they could have careers. As a young man, you deprived me of love. And as a man you prevented me from having faith and confidence in myself. You despoiled even my name, converting it into an outlandish and wretched nickname: Waxy Cord!

"I spoke—and others took my words as their own. I did good—and others received the rewards.

"How often I suffered punishment for crimes which others had committed.

"I had friends who sought me out when they were hungry and in their hours of plenty, they turned their backs on me.

"People gathered around me, as if I were a clown, so that I could make them laugh with the stories of my adventures. But never, never did anyone dry a single one of my tears!

"Humanity, I stole some money from you; I made fun of you; my vices ridiculed you. I do not repent! And at the very moment of my death, I wish

I had the strength to spit all of my scorn into your face.

"I was Pito Perez: a shadow that passed from jail to jail, hungry! Waxy Cord: a great sorrow made happy by the tinkling of bells!

"I was a drunkard. A nobody! A walking truth. What madness! And there, walking on the other side of the road, Honesty displayed her decorum and Wisdom showed off her prudence. The struggle has been unequal, and this I understand. But out of the mettle of the humble there will surge one day an earthquake and then no stone will remain upon another.

"Humanity, I shall soon collect what you owe me!

Jesus Perez Gaona

Morelia, the . . ."

And mixed in with the dust of the earth, the useless ashes of a man were lost forever . . .

Biography
of
JOSÉ RUBÉN ROMERO
1890–1952

To know the history of Mexico during the first half of the twentieth century is to know the works of José Rubén Romero. To comprehend this history, is to know his life as well. Indeed, today Romero is a permanent figure in the annals and archives of that land of incredible horizons, famed above all for his talent for recording in words the very marrow of modern Mexico.

Paradoxically, Romero was a person of complex intellectual configuration and a man of simple heart and generous spirit. He may be viewed from many vantage points: businessman and politician, revolutionary and seeker of peace, diplomat, poet, orator, essayist, novelist, promoter of the humor that is singularly Mexican, advisor to presidents, counselor to nations, colleague of royalty. But, above all else, Rubén Romero was a man of human qualities: a kind of hero to the humble and the poor, a friend of all mankind, a man who lived and loved the unique flavor of the provincial life of his country.

Although in some books of political history Romero is described as the originator and interpreter of a new kind of national and international diplomacy, his name in literary history is of greater import. It is he who more than any other man of letters interpreted the essence of contemporary Mexico. It is he who perceived in his people a transcendental virtue which had survived four hundred years of subjugation. He saw more than mere deeds and events. He felt the pulse of his nation. And he wrote with a sensitivity which reflected intimacy but excluded the statistics of the encyclopedic mind; he described the vital nature of his Mexico, but left to the historians the matters of names and dates and times. If, for some, Romero is a *popular* writer, he is also that author who has been called the "Voice of Mexico" and the "Voice for Mexico." Indeed, for many, José Rubén Romero *is* Mexico.

Romero, the son of a general storekeeper, was born on September 25, 1890, in the isolated village of Cotija de la Paz in the central state of Michoacán. From the beginning, his sturdy parents instilled in him the importance of the human qualities of kindness, sensitivity, and understanding, qualities which framed the basic attitude with which Romero, throughout his life, approached all problems.

In 1898, the family moved to Mexico City and remained there until 1904. During those six years in the Mexican capital, young Romero had his first taste of cosmopolitan life. He explored all the corners of that great city, inspecting, observing, participating in all the activites that can be a part of youth in a metropolis. It was also during those years that Romero took his first literary steps in what would one day become a pathway to international recognition. Always an avid reader, and having listened so often to his mother as she read aloud, he now began to compose short, simple four-line verses.

In 1904, after six years of rather arduous labors and a frugal life in the Mexican capital, Romero's father decided that the family should return to Michoacán. The family moved to Ario de Rosales and, from that time until 1919, Romero was to live in several cities of Michoacán: Pátzcuaro, Sahuayo, Santa Clara del Cobre, Morelia, Tacámbaro.

For young José, the return to Michoacán was to be the key which would open completely the door for those desires which had been hidden within him. It was in Ario that Romero began in earnest to develop his talents for creative writing. All that he had seen, all that he had heard, all that he had read, all that had been read to him, and all that he had lived now awakened within him a fervent and ardent desire to write. Here in Ario, he began to compose more verses—with all the vitality that a youth of serious intent and fifteen years of age can boast. Naturally enough, in all of these verses there was but one single theme: young love. But, intermingled in these amorous declarations, a certain artistic sensibility is discernible, a certain aesthetic faculty which permitted the poet to enjoy the simple beauties which he found so bountiful in provincial life.

Although poetry had been thus far the vehicle for Romero's romantic laments, in 1906 he began to write prose. These were short pieces, usually of one page. They were not stories with plot and characters in the usual sense, but rather sensations which he had at some time felt or perhaps dreamed. If these writings contributed to his later literary triumphs in that they afforded him practice in the complex art of creative writing, their only real merit at this time lay in the indication that Romero was seeking another form of expression, searching for another means to communicate more fully and completely.

By 1908, Romero's name as a poet was widespread in Michoacán. His works had been published in most of the major newspapers and in that year he published his first book of poetry, *Fantasías*.

And now, a young adult of eighteen, Romero was a sociable individual: sympathetic, kind, humble, eager to listen to the tragedies of the lives of others and equally eager to help all persons in their day-to-day existence. He was also a man of subtle humor and quick wit, a teller-of-tales who savored the piquancy of off-color stories, a kind of burlesque *don Juan*, a young man who sought the applause of the people and the considerations of the young ladies. He was an alert, energetic individual, an avid consumer of the potent drinks of the region and a person who favored with gusto the uniqueness of Mexican cuisine.

In 1911, Romero openly declared himself in favor of Francisco Madero's actions against the dictatorship and tyranny of Porfirio Díaz. With this declaration and his subsequent activities under General Escalante, Rubén Romero made himself a part of the Mexican Revolution. In 1912, he affiliated himself with Miguel Silva, a candidate for the governorship of Michoacán. Silva won the election and appointed Romero his private secretary. This was Romero's introduction into the world of Mexican politics.

The paucity of official obligations afforded him time to continue writing and publishing. Separate poems appeared in the newspapers and journals and late in 1912 he published two more volumes of his verses: *Hojas Marchitas* (*Withered Leaves*) a small book of eleven poems which he dedicated to his brother and sister, Federico and Rebeca, and *Rimas bohemias*.

Shortly after the Decena Trágica of February 1913, in which Victoriano Huerta had taken the presidency from the assassinated Madero, a new political flavor was injected into the Revolution. As a follower of Madero, Romero was considered a conspirator against the government and was forced to seek refuge in Mexico City. Without funds in the captial city, Romero spent almost a year literally living from hand-to-mouth. In August 1914, the political situation had improved and Romero considered it favorable for his return to Michoacán, to Tacámbaro where he was to live until 1919.

While in Tacámbaro, Romero continued to write and to publish his poetry. In addition to the individual works published in the journals and newspapers of the region, he published privately, in 1915, a book of short stories, *Cuentos Rurales* (*Stories of the Countryside*). The volume attracted little attention and today no copies of this work are known to exist.

During these several years in Tacámbaro, Romero served in several minor positions in the local government and continued to promote the cause of the Revolution. His name and his work as a revolutionary soon came to the attention of the major officials of Michoacán and he received several state and federal commissions to attend official meetings and conventions as a representative of the Revolutionary Party.

In 1917, Romero published two more volumes of poetry, *La Musa Loca* (*The Insane Muse*) and *Alma Heroica* (*Heroic Soul*), a short but eloquent poetic tribute to the village of Tacámbaro. There was now a noticeable change in his topics and ideas. A certain maturity was evident and a more definite crystalization of ideas was apparent.

But a change in the course of his life was about to occur. In July 1919, Pascual Ortiz Rubio, Governor of Michoacán and later President of the Republic, named Romero representative from Michoacán to the Federal Commission which maintained its headquarters in Mexico City. It was because of this appointment that Romero was now to leave Morelia to establish a home in the Mexican capital and, in essence, was never again to reside in his beloved state of Michoacán.

Romero's new life in the Mexican capital almost put an end to his poetic efforts. Although he did publish, in 1919, another volume of verses, *Sentimental,* his obligations in his new position and the diversity of amusements in the city left him little time for writing. In 1920, he was appointed Inspector General of the Department of Public Communications. Later in the same year, under the supervision of his personal friend Alvaro Obregón, he was promoted to Chief of the Department of Publicity and then to the Department of Foreign Relations, which was to be a training ground for future assignments.

In 1922, at the insistence of Obregón, he published his last volume of original poetry, *Tacámbaro*, admittedly inspired by the pleasant years he had spent in that village. It was a volume of that verse known as *hai-ku*, popular in the literature of the Orient.

Political advancement came rapidly to Romero. In 1923, he was appointed to the Department of the Exterior and between 1924 and 1930 he continued to be advanced on his political ladder until he reached the Administrative Office of the President of Mexico. In 1930, he was appointed a candidate for the governorship of Michoacán, appointment by the President being tantamount to election. Romero declined the candidacy and continued his work with the federal government in Mexico City.

In April of 1930, President Pascual Ortiz Rubio offered Romero the position of Consul General in Barcelona, Spain. He arrived in La Coruña, Spain, on September 15, 1930. Four days later in the Palace of San Sebastian, Romero was officially received by His Majesty, Alfonso XIII, King of Spain.

Although Rubén Romero found life in Spain exciting and stimulating, his deep-seated love for the life of the province seemed to haunt him constantly. Romero himself once said that when he left Mexico he began to see in it a beauty he had never before noticed.

The product of this nostalgia was Romero's first novel, *Apuntes de un lugareño* (*The Notes of a Vil-*

lage Lad). Working now in prose, Romero felt more at ease. He found this new medium an easy task and he felt there was no need for the linguistic polish basic to poetry. And in this new form, Romero discovered the literary vehicle in which he could express himself more fully and with which he could communicate more completely, the medium by which eventually he would obtain immortality in the world of literature.

In 1934, he began work on his second novel, *Desbandada* (*At Random*), which was published in the same year. This work the author described as a series of pictures in which he attempted to preserve the memories of the happy years of his life in Tacámbaro. Like his first novel, *Desbandada* was an immediate success. It received extremely favorable criticism and reviews in Mexico and abroad, and definitely established Romero as one of Mexico's potentially great novelists. Late in 1934, in Spain, Romero wrote and published the third of his novels, *El pueblo inocente* (*The Innocent Village*), a work whose theme had been taken from the history of Ario de Rosales during the bitter, fighting days of the Revolution.

As a result of these novels, established critics praised highly the talent that was Romero's. One critic even predicted that if Romero continued writing in the vein and style found in these first works, he would become the novelist of modern Mexico most to be envied by all other writers. In November of

1934, no less an organization than the Mexican Academy of Language (Academia Mexicana de la Lengua, Correspondiente de la Española) recommended Romero as a non-voting member of this famous and exclusive chamber. This recommendation was approved on August 7, 1935, and Romero took his place among the eighteen members allowed in this capacity.

The following year, 1936, while still serving as Consul General in Barcelona, Romero published the fourth of his novels, *Mi caballo, mi perro, y mi rifle* (*My Horse, My Dog, and My Gun*). In this work, Romero broadened somewhat the scope of his previous themes. His perspective of the Revolution was greater and his imagination played a more important role in the development of the theme and characters.

But as Romero's literary fame had continued to grow, so the difficulties of his governmental position in Spain had become more complex. In the last few months of 1936, when the conflict had reached a climax, Romero felt the strained relationship between that country and Mexico. In December of that year, he left Spain. He was received in Mexico by his government and his countrymen as one of Mexico's celebrated novelists.

Shortly after his arrival from Spain, he was called to the office of Avila Camacho, a leading figure of Mexican politics and a future President of the Republic. Camacho asked Romero to assume the Rectorship of the University of Michoacán. Within a matter of months Romero had settled certain disturbances which had beset the school and he was then appointed Mexico's Ambassador to Brazil.

In Brazil, as in Spain, Romero found himself haunted by nostalgia for his homeland. The urge to write again was with him. He decided to create a novel of distinct theme, flavor, and style. He proposed a plot and attempted to develop it in a literary style of a most polished character. When he had written the first few pages of this new work, he read them aloud to one of Cuba's ministers who was serving in Brazil. When the latter dozed and his head sagged, Romero knew he was not convincing in this new form. He destroyed what he had written and turned again to the people of Michoacán for inspiration. In six weeks he had finished the work which he was to call a book of little significance, one which had been written with the hope that people read it and perhaps laugh at some of the antics and remark about some of the language. The novel was *La vida inútil de Pito Pérez* (*The Futile Life of Pito Perez*), the story of a man whom he had known and, in a unique manner, had admired in the distant village of Santa Clara del Cobre.

With this novel, Rubén Romero reached the peak of his literary career and introduced to the world the unforgettable personage of Jesús Pérez Gaona, alias Pito Pérez, whose story is that of a man embittered

143

by much that was done in a society whose false values he could not accept, a man who is at once authentically Mexican in background and development, as well as universal in ideals and popular philosophy. And, if Pito allowed himself to stray from the rigid pathways of society's rules, it was an escape from social hypocrisy, for such was his character that never would he relinquish one iota of his belief in the two factors he valued most in life: honesty of self and true dignity of conscience.

Despite the tremendous literary acclaim which was now given to Romero, he continued his association with the federal government of Mexico. In 1938, he was appointed Mexico's Ambassador to Cuba. As Ambassador, Romero soon became the symbol of friendship between the countries of Benito Juárez and José Martí. While in Cuba, in 1939, he completed another novel, *Anticipación a la muerte* (*Anticipation of Death*), a novel which on the surface may appear to be dominated by an aspect of morbidity. But the subtle humor which Romero brings to the fore displaces whatever air of gloom is suggested.

During his service in Cuba, another of Romero's talents made itself known. Because of his open and cordial friendliness, he was called upon to speak before groups and organizations of all kinds. Within a brief period of time, he became one of the most popular orators in Cuba. Romero talked about

144

Mexico—a Mexico conscious of the fact that human beings, in the course of their daily lives, are many times successfully tempted to act purely for themselves at the expense of others. But, also a Mexico that had forgotten how to hate and had learned to forgive.

Naturally, during the course of his work in Cuba, he returned to Mexico from time to time to consult with his superiors and to visit with old friends. In August of 1941, a special reception was held for him in the Palace of Fine Arts in the Mexican capital. At this reception, Romero read a recently completed work which was to become one of the most popular and respected of all his writings. He titled the work *Semblanza de una mujer (Portrait of a Woman)*. In this paper, he spoke of his mother and of the training and counsel she had given him from his early youth through his mature life. It was more than a speech; it was the eulogy of a dedicated son. When Romero had finished his reading there was a brief period of absolute silence. Then, the audience rose and awarded him a tremendous ovation which continued for several minutes. He related later that tears had come to his eyes, not because he had presented a good speech, but because he had been able to express to an understanding audience the most intimate of thoughts and feelings for that person who had given him most in this life.

In 1942, while serving in Havana, he completed

another novel, *Una vez fuí rico* (*Once I Was a Rich Man*). Although it is the only work which critics have accepted as a true novel in the contemporary literary meaning of the word, it contributes little if any enhancement to Romero's stature as a novelist.

Rubén Romero continued his diplomatic obligations in Havana. By 1944, he was known throughout the entire island as the most effective diplomat ever sent to Cuba by any country. Indeed, he had reached the high point of international acclaim in the world of politics and government.

But all this was to end suddenly. On October 31, 1944, on the front page of one of Mexico City's most important newspapers, the following news item appeared:

> The Secretary of Foreign Affairs announced that by decision of the President of the Reppublic, the Commission of José Rubén Romero as Ambassador of our country to the Government of the Republic of Cuba has been terminated.

The entire nation was stunned at the news and thrown into a complete turmoil as to what actually had occurred regarding this man held in such high esteem by the people of Mexico and the people of Cuba. The "Romero Case," as it was soon called, became the singular topic of conversation and discussion throughout the Republic of Mexico. There was speculation that Romero had been dismissed by President Camacho. There was speculation that he had been dismissed by other persons in the Department of Foreign Affairs. There was also speculation that Romero had resigned. Although full disclosures were never made, Romero nevertheless was no longer Mexico's Ambassador to Cuba.

It is true that after his dismissal Rubén Romero never again regained the political rank and stature that had once been his. Although his dismissal was of personal concern to him and to his friends, Romero openly admitted that if his work could be accomplished with greater efficiency by others, he would comply most willingly with his government's request. Mexico had always been his primary concern and his confidence in its leaders allowed him to accept in true faith the decision that had been made.

President Camacho did not separate Romero completely from the federal government. He appointed Romero to be one of his private advisers and on many occasions Romero was commissioned Mexico's official delegate on missions of federal and diplomatic concern. In 1946, he was re-appointed adviser to the president by the newly elected head of State, Miguel Alemán, and in this capacity he journeyed extensively throughout the country with the President on official missions.

Romero's withdrawal from the high echelons of his government did not deter him from further literary efforts. In 1946 he published his last novel,

Rosenda. Although it was a novel with little plot, it was considered the most serious of all his works. It was a novel which expressed the tender sensitivities of a humble, illiterate girl and the affection which grew between her and her benefactor, Romero, as he attempted successfully to teach her to read and to write and, later, how the qualities of honesty, dignity, and integrity are indeed more valuable to man than the accumulation of material things which may be a part of the lives of others.

Rosenda was Romero's last novel, but it did not signify a termination of his literary career. In 1948, he contracted to write a series of articles for the magazine *Hoy.* His career as a journalist began on January 3 of that year and continued until January 30, 1951, during which time his weekly essays appeared in the magazine. Romero was excited with this new vehicle for the expression of his ideas. His articles, which were really popular essays, gave him freedom to record many of the matters which he had not been able to include in his poetry or his novels. He stated that it was his intent in this series of articles to write on as many aspects of twentieth-century Mexico as possible. These articles were read avidly by the public and in their totality they reflect a generic compendium of the contemporary culture and civilization of Mexico.

After some fifty years of writing and contributing to the *belles lettres* of Mexican literature, Romero received what he considered to be the singular honor of his lifetime. On June 14, 1950, the Mexican Academy of Language unanimously voted to elevate him from the rank of non-voting member of the Chamber to the stature of *académico de número*. In the culture and tradition of Mexico, to be one of the thirty-six members of the Academy is in itself public acknowledgement of significant literary prestige. To be elevated to the numbered chairs is an honor achieved by only a few of the outstanding writers of the country, and then only by those whose works are possessed of the qualities and characteristics recognized by universal standards and acclaim.

Romero was yet to experience another avenue of expression. In June of 1952, he contracted with a radio station in Mexico City to give a weekly address. In these informal recorded chats, he was to speak on topics of his choosing and was given complete freedom to expose his ideas and comments on the history, civilization, and culture of Mexico as he had observed and lived it.

During the fourth week of his broadcasts, on July 1, 1952, Romero suffered a blood clot. He was given medication and ordered to remain at home in relative quiet. On July 4, 1952, however, he left his home and reported to the studio to record a speech in which he paid special homage to his friend of the distant past, Miguel Silva. At 4:30 that afternoon he left his home secretly and went to a jai-alai game which he had wanted very much to see. At 7:30 that evening, while in the sports arena, he suffered a heart attack. At 8:00 o'clock on the evening of July 4, 1952, as his recorded words on Miguel Silva went out over the airways of Mexico, José Rubén Romero died.

José Rubén Romero was buried in the Panteón Francés de la Piedad in Mexico City. The funeral oration was read by another of Mexico's famous writers, José Vasconselos, who spoke of his warm friendship for Romero, and of his great admiration for Romero's contributions to Mexico's Golden Age of Literature.

Thus death had come to Rubén Romero, a man who by his own admission had never had intense intellectual powers. He was a person possessed of the nobility of heart which he considered to be the epitome of man's purpose on earth, a man who practiced a benign attitude toward the frailties of human nature. This personal philosophy caused him to see only good in mankind.

Of his devotion to his country there can be no doubt. He supported the cause of Mexico. He saw modern Mexico as an uneasy, contradictory country —even austere. And he also admitted that his fatherland was a country in which the incredibility of paradox existed within all facets of life, yet it was that very paradox which gave Mexico a charm and elegance unequaled elsewhere in the world. And, in the twentieth century, it was in the Revolution that he discovered the foundation on which Mexico could emerge and stand as a free and individual nation. In the Revolution Romero saw the composition of a great Mexican rhapsody: a literature, an art, a music, a dance, and most important and significant of all, out of this Revolution had come a people who, despite the tragedy of four hundred years, had fused and joined together to work toward a limitless future and had caused the chronicle of the day to be recorded in many forms.

Romero's literary genius has never ceased to stimulate and inspire scholars. His concept of essence, of totality, is everywhere apparent. If, in fact, the polish, the scrupulous style of literary art is not found, there is in its place a chronicle that is spontaneous and contemporary, filled with the figure of twentieth-century Mexico.

But, of all the fame that Romero had acquired, of all the status he had achieved, of all the respect and admiration which was given him in his country and abroad, he preferred, above all else, to be known as a patriot of Mexico. He once wrote that his greatest ambition was only to have his name come forth, like the faint tinkling of a little bell, at the slightest movement of his fatherland. The bells of Pito Pérez have sounded and José Rubén Romero has realized his ambition.

W. O. C.

Morelia, Michoacán
Republic of Mexico
and Rohnert Park, California
September 1966